Reading

for Christian Schools 2-2

Bob Jones University Press, Greenville, South Carolina 29614

Consultants

from the administration and faculty of Bob Jones University

Grace C. Collins, Ph.D., *Chairman, Department of Linguistics*
Walter G. Fremont, Ed.D., *Dean of the School of Education*
Melva M. Heintz, M.A., *Elementary Principal*
Janice A. Joss, M.A.T., *Graduate School of Education*
Betty Anne Rupp, M.A., *Professor of Reading, School of Education*
Philip D. Smith, Ed.D., *Provost*
Hazel M. Truman, M.A., *Project Director, University Press*

Houghton Mifflin Company: Glossary material based on the lexical database of the *Children's Dictionary,* copyright ©1981 Houghton Mifflin Company. No part of this book may be reproduced or transmitted in any form or by any means, electronic or mechanical, including photocopying and recording, or by any information storage or retrieval system, except as may be expressly permitted by the 1976 Copyright Act or with prior written permission from both Houghton Mifflin Company and the Bob Jones University Press.

"The Picnic." Reprinted from *Hop, Skip, and Jump.* The editors tried to obtain permission to use this poem, but without success.

READING for Christian Schools® 2-2
Produced in cooperation with the Bob Jones University School of Education and Bob Jones Elementary School.

©1983 Bob Jones University Press
Greenville, South Carolina 29614

Printed in the United States of America

ISBN 0-89084-187-X

20   19   18   17   16   15   14   13   12   11   10

CONTENTS

Coastal Lands

Special Deeds

Making Melody

COASTAL LANDS

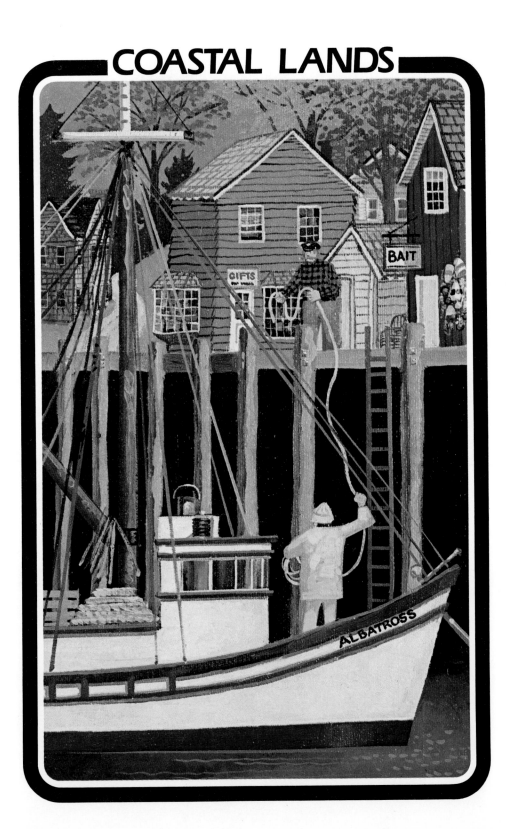

Hurricane!
Storm's Coming

Jane and Randy splashed from puddle to puddle outside their house. Jane squealed with excitement as water flew everywhere.

"Storm's coming! Storm's coming!" Jane chanted with each splash.

"Jane, Randy," called their mother.

The two wet, excited children raced to the porch. They took off their soaking wet raincoats and boots and went into the house.

"Randy, please turn on the radio," said Mrs. Parker. "We need to find out where the storm is now."

In the middle of a program, a man began to speak. "We interrupt this program for the latest news. The storm off the coast is now a hurricane. It is moving toward the north. Keep your radio on for further news."

"Will we have to go to a shelter this time?" Randy gave his mother a worried look.

"I don't know yet," replied his mother. "We will keep the radio on. Your father will know if we should leave or stay here." She patted Randy on the arm. "The Lord will take care of us."

The kitchen door slammed. Mr. Parker stepped inside the kitchen.

"Dad," said Randy. "Did you hear the news? A hurricane is coming!"

"Yes, Randy," replied Mr. Parker. "I heard the news on the car radio. We have a lot of work to do before dark."

"What can I do, Dad?" asked Randy.

"You can pick up everything in the yard that the wind could blow away. Put everything in the shed, even the trash cans. Jane can help you."

Jane and Randy went outside. Randy carried the trash cans to the shed. Jane splashed behind him, carrying a lawn chair. At every step, she chanted, "Storm's coming!"

4

When nothing was left to put away, they went to find their father. He was on the other side of the house, taping the windows.

"Why do you always put tape on the windows before a storm, Daddy?" asked Jane.

"Tape keeps the glass from flying everywhere if the window cracks," replied Mr. Parker. He tossed a roll of tape to Randy. "If you will finish taping the outside, I will tape the inside of the windows."

"Okay, Dad," Randy grinned.

5

Jane went inside with Mr. Parker. Mrs. Parker looked up as they came in.

"We have plenty of food," she said. "There are still lots of batteries for the flashlight and the radio. I don't think we need anything from the store."

"Good," said Mr. Parker. "The wind is already beginning to blow."

When all the work was finished everyone gathered in the kitchen. It was late by the time they sat down for supper. During supper the wind began to blow harder. Broken palm branches blew across the yard.

The Storm

"I'm glad we picked everything up," said Randy.

Mr. Parker turned the radio up louder. "Winds from the hurricane are now reaching the coast," said the announcer. "The hurricane is still heading north. It has not turned toward land. There is no need to go to a shelter at this time. However, we can expect high winds and heavy rain. Please keep your radio on."

After supper Mrs. Parker got the children's sleeping bags. "You may sleep down here tonight," she said.

Jane and Randy hurried through their baths. Soon they were tucked into the warm sleeping bags. After praying, Mrs. Parker sang softly to them. Their tired eyes closed and they slept.

Before dawn the wind began howling. The noise woke the children. They went to the kitchen where Mr. and Mrs. Parker were sitting.

"The wind is really loud," said Jane. "It woke us up."

"Maybe it's looking for something to eat like I am," said Randy.

"You and Jane run upstairs and get some playclothes. We will eat early this morning since Randy is so hungry. We will be ready to eat by the time you are dressed," said Mrs. Parker.

By the time the children got back, bacon was sizzling in the pan.

"Mmm," said Randy. He and Jane sat down at the table. While everyone was eating, the lights flickered and went out.

"Stay still while I light the candles," said Mr. Parker.

Soon bright flames glowed in the dim light. Mr. Parker turned up the radio.

"The hurricane is still moving up the coast," said the announcer. "Stay inside. Keep your radio on for more news of the storm."

"Since the power is off, the stove won't work," said Mrs. Parker.

"I'm glad we got to eat," said Randy. "Is this what it was like when you were a boy?"

"No," laughed Mr. Parker. "It's more like when my grandfather was a boy. People really lived without electric lights, radio, and the telephone."

Mrs. Parker carried the candles to the living room. Jane curled up on Mother's lap. Randy sat quietly by Mr. Parker's feet. Mr. Parker began to tell stories he had been told when he was growing up.

The wind began to howl and blow even louder.

"The wind roars like a lion," whispered Jane.

"Like a hungry lion!" teased Randy.

"Let's sing some songs," said Mr. Parker. "Then the wind won't seem so loud to you."

They sang song after song. Suddenly they heard a crash!

Jane clutched her mother fearfully. Randy sat up. "What was that?" he asked.

Mr. Parker went to the window to look. "Just a tree falling," he said. "Let's pray again and ask God to give us courage."

"Dear Lord," he prayed, "You promised to be with us always. Help us not to be afraid. Teach us to trust You. In Jesus' name. Amen."

Discovery

"Now it's Mother's turn to tell a story," said Mr. Parker.

Mrs. Parker smiled. "What story would you like to hear?"

"David and the giant," said Randy.

"Yes, David and the giant," said Jane. The two children settled down as Mrs. Parker began to speak.

At last they stopped for a snack. Mrs. Parker set a tray on the table. There were sandwiches, pears, and four glasses of milk.

"The wind isn't as loud," said Randy.

"Is the storm over?" asked Jane.

"Not yet," said Mr. Parker. "It's still raining. But it looks like the hurricane missed us. Listen!"

"The hurricane is now headed out to sea," said the radio announcer.

"Hooray!" cried the children.

Mrs. Parker laughed. "Since you have to stay inside, why don't you draw pictures for a while?"

Late in the afternoon the rain slowed down to a drizzle. Everyone put on raincoats and boots. They went outside to explore.

"Everything looks different," said Randy.

Jane sniffed the air. "It smells different too. Clean and fresh."

"Look!" cried Jane. "There is the tree the wind blew over!" She ran to the fallen tree. "I can climb a tree now," she said excitedly.

Jane walked up and down the tree trunk. Randy explored the roots. He poked at the little bugs scurrying up and down.

14

"Come down here," called Mrs. Parker from the beach. The children scrambled down to join their mother and father.

The beach was covered with shells, seaweed, and jellyfish.

"They were swept up by the waves," said Mrs. Parker. "Look!"

She pointed to a rainbow-colored jellyfish lying on the wet sand.

"And an old piece of wood!" cried Randy. "Do you think it came from an old wrecked ship?"

"Maybe," Mr. Parker smiled.

The family spent the rest of the afternoon on the wet beach, collecting treasures from the sea. They watched the big waves that still pounded along the shore. At last they climbed the path to the house.

"I'm glad the storm is over, but it was a safe feeling to stay together inside the house," said Randy.

"Storms make us depend on the Lord more," Mr. Parker said. "I think that is why He sends them."

Jane splashed on up the path. "God loves us!" she chanted. "God loves us! He sends big storms, but He loves us!"

16

A Tide Pool

During the night the tide came in. Seawater crashed over the rocks. Waves rippled farther and farther up the beach. At last they spread their lacy foam to the high-water mark. Then slowly, slowly, the water returned to the sea.

Not all the water went back out with the tide. Some water was caught in deep holes between the rocks. This trapped water is called a *tide pool*.

Each day the tide brings fresh seawater into the pools. The small sea animals that live in the pools get their food from the seawater. God has given each of these sea animals special ways to survive.

Let's take a look at a tide pool.

Look! Is that an orange under the ledge? No, when you touch it, it moves! When it is in danger, the sea anemone pulls in its little tentacles. Then it looks like an old orange. When the danger is gone, the sea anemone will open up. Then it looks like a beautiful flower.

God made the tentacles to help feed the sea anemone. The tentacles wave back and forth in the water. They sting small animals that come too close. The animals will be the sea anemone's next meal.

Another animal in the tide pool is the sea urchin. During the tides it clings to the rocks and will not let go. This keeps it from being swept away. When the water is still, the sea urchin moves slowly along the bottom of the pool.

When the sea urchin is in danger it hides between the rocks. But it does not really have to fear its enemies. It has so many spikes that it looks like a prickly pincushion.

How wonderful it is that God takes care of the animals of the sea!

Now look over there on the rocks. Could those be fallen stars? The five arms of the starfish make them look like stars. Along the arms are many tiny sucker-like feet. Water helps the feet of the starfish stick tightly to the rocks. Starfish sometimes break off an arm. A new arm will grow in place of the old one.

Over there are some beautiful shells. A clam lives inside each closed shell. The clams will open their shells when the tide covers their pool. The clams open their shells to take in water. They eat tiny plants from the water. Then they spit the water back out.

Maybe someday you can visit a tide pool. Will you remember what animals live there? Will you remember how clams eat?

Could you find a "pincushion" or a "flower" in the water? Could you see an "orange" or a "star"? Could you tell your mom and dad what they really are? Don't forget to tell them how God keeps these animals safe!

Mystery in the Attic

The Whaler's Chest

"Moving has been hard work," Joel said. "We've been putting things away for four days!"

"I'm glad we're done. Now we can explore the attic while Mother is baking," Keith said.

"Mother is baking cookies," said Ricky.

"I know." Keith grinned at his little brother. "We'll come back down when they are ready to eat."

The three boys climbed the creaky stairs. They stopped on the landing to look out the window. The gray waves rushed up on the shore below. Low gray clouds drifted in from the sea.

"It's getting foggy," said Joel. "Let's pretend we're on a ship lost in the fog."

"Wait until we get to the attic," Keith said. He started up the stairs again.

A foghorn blew far away. "Did you hear that?" Joel asked.

Ricky moved closer to Keith.

Keith brushed a cobweb out of the way. "That's just to signal the boats not to get too close to the rocks," he said.

"I like this new-old house," Joel said.

"New-old house!" Keith laughed.

Joel smiled. "It's new to us, but it's old because it was built a long time ago. It would have been fun to live way back then."

"Here we are," said Keith. He gave the attic door a push. It creaked slowly open.

Joel and Ricky peered around him.

"Look at that!" cried Joel. "This place is full of old stuff!"

"I want to go downstairs," said Ricky. "Maybe the cookies are done."

"Come on, Ricky." Keith went into the attic. "We'll find something for you to play with."

Joel and Ricky followed him through the doorway.

"There's a chest by those old chairs,"

Keith said. He went over to look. "It has a name and an address on it. 'Dr. Eli Greene, 11 Brook Ave., Bridgeport, Maine.'"

"That's our address," Joel said. "Dr. Greene must have lived here a long time ago."

The rusty hinges creaked as the boys raised the lid and peered inside. Everything lay in a tangled heap at the bottom of the chest.

Keith pulled out a long rope and handed it to Ricky. Ricky walked around the chest dragging the rope behind him. "See my big snake?" he asked.

Keith reached into the chest again. He pulled out a bent metal hoop, a lamp, and a torn picture album.

Joel picked up the album. "These pictures look like our new house," he said, carefully turning the faded pages. "But our house has taller trees around it."

"And it doesn't have that tower on the roof," Keith added. He looked at the pictures thoughtfully. "I wonder if—"

A-Whaling We Go!

Keith jumped as Ricky dropped the rope across his feet.

"I want to play with something else," said Ricky.

"How about playing with this old lamp?" asked Keith. He handed it to Ricky.

Joel put the album down. "With the rope and lamp we could pretend that we are whalers," he said. "We could be whalers out on the high seas. The attic can be our whaling ship."

"Okay," said Keith. "The chimney will be the mast." He pretended to light the lamp for Ricky. Ricky set it on an old chair.

Just then the foghorn blew loudly and Joel jumped. "Well, mates, you should be more careful. We don't want to run aground. The fog is so thick our ship will hit a whale before we see it."

Ricky and Keith laughed.

"Oh, this storm is making me seasick," Joel moaned. He rolled onto a creaky cot. "Will we ever reach land? I think we are lost at sea."

Ricky jumped on top of him.

"Ouch," cried Joel. The cot tipped over and both boys fell onto the floor.

"Be still, you two," said Keith. He pointed to the other end of the attic. "Look at that! There is a door in the roof and a wooden peg with something hanging on it. It looks like a spyglass."

"Why would a spyglass be hanging there? There aren't any stairs to reach it," Joel said.

"Maybe the door goes outside to the roof," Keith said. "Let's go outside and look at the door from the ground."

The three boys scrambled down the stairs and out the door. Thick fog rolled in from the shore.

"Can you see the door?" Joel asked.

"No, I can't see anything in this fog."
Keith squinted his eyes.

The boys hurried back inside.

"Come on, Ricky," Keith said. "Let's go back upstairs."

"I'm hungry," said Ricky, sniffing the air.

"You can stay down here with Mother if you want to," Keith said. He and Joel started up the stairs.

Ricky gave a longing look toward the kitchen. "Wait for me," he called, following them up the stairs.

"Grandpa is asleep and Dad won't be home from work until five o'clock," Joel said. "We will have to find out about the mystery door ourselves."

"Well, I'm going to explore," Keith said. "Maybe I can find a clue. Why don't you look by the chimney, Joel? I'll check by the window."

Keith poked around the boxes for a while. He pushed the chairs aside. "Joel, Ricky, come here," he called. "Here is an old desk. It has been shoved back against the wall."

Clues and a Letter

Joel and Ricky ran to see. Joel opened the little cubbyholes and cabinets in the desk.

"There is nothing here after all," Joel said. "Just an empty desk."

"Wait." Keith bent over. He pulled a yellow piece of paper from behind a drawer. "This was stuck," he said, turning the crumpled paper over in his hand. "There are some words on it. It's an old letter."

"Boys!" Grandpa called from the hallway. "Your mother made some cookies. Who would like some?"

"Me!" yelled Ricky. The door slammed behind him and he clumped down the stairs.

Keith tucked the letter into his pocket. He and Joel climbed down to the landing.

"You two are moving slowly," Grandpa chuckled. "Ricky almost flew by."

"We found an old letter," Keith said.

"Yes, we're on the trail of the attic mystery," Joel added.

"The mystery of the door in the roof," Keith said.

"Attic mystery?" Grandpa asked as Keith handed him the letter. He pulled out his reading glasses and put them on. Tilting his head to see, he began to read.

Dear Dr. Greene,

I hope your new house is almost completed. Will you be staying on shore now, or will you still go whaling?

I hope you put a tower in your house. You will be able to look across the water and see ships coming in. I hang my spyglass from a peg by the door of my tower.

I plan to visit Bridgeport soon. I will stop to visit you then.

Yours truly,

Mr. Edwin Fenning

"Once there was a tower on this house," Keith said as Grandpa finished reading. "The door went to the tower. Come and look, Grandpa."

Grandpa followed the two boys up the stairs.

"Dr. Greene must have followed Mr. Fenning's advice," Keith said. He pointed to the door in the roof. "So that *is* a spyglass hanging on the wooden peg by the door! It must be as old as this house."

Joel picked up the faded picture book. "The house with the little trees and the tower must be this house," he said.

"You boys have done a fine job of finding where the mystery door led," Grandpa said. "The tower is gone now. It must have been torn down. The door will not open now." He looked out the window. "I think the fog is clearing. When your father comes home, we will get the spyglass down for you. Right now, let's go down before Ricky eats all the cookies!"

The Promised Land

(based on historical research)

On the Mayflower

Seven-year-old Richard More huddled in the hold of the *Mayflower* with the other Pilgrims. He shivered in the cold, damp air.

Richard looked around. He saw Remember Allerton, a little girl only six years old. She sat in a corner close by, hugging her knees. A tear slid slowly down her cheek.

Richard went to her side. "Why do you cry, Remember?" he asked gently.

"My mother is sick. My clothes are sticky and smelly. And worms are in our food." Remember's voice was no more than a whisper, for she knew she should not be complaining.

"We will be in America soon," Richard said. "God will take care of us."

Before Richard could say any more, someone cried out, "Listen! I hear something!"

It was a sailor they heard, high up in the ship's crow's nest. "Land ho!" His call sounded above the beating waves. "Land ho!"

"Land!" Sailors screamed and threw their hats up in the air.

"Land!" Pilgrims shouted and hugged each other.

The ladder leading from the hold to the deck was suddenly crowded with people. Everyone wanted to get to the railing where they could see this land for themselves.

The misty blue coasts became clearer as the ship sailed closer and closer.

There it was—America!

"It is our Promised Land!" Mr. Brewster cried. "The Lord has safely led us here. Let us gather together and sing a psalm of thanksgiving." The Pilgrims sang and worshiped the Lord.

Just as they finished, a seagull flew above their heads. The children laughed as four more seagulls dived at the ship. Each one screeched its harsh cry and then flew back toward shore.

Six-year-old Wrestling Brewster jumped up and down. He flapped his arms, pretending he had wings.

"The seagulls are saying 'Hurry up! Hurry up! Get to America!'"

"Mr. Brewster, may we go to shore tomorrow?" Richard looked up with pleading eyes.

"Oh, yes, Mr. Brewster! Tomorrow may we go ashore? Oh yes, please, please!" Almost twenty children suddenly crowded around the pilgrim leader, hands clasped, eyes begging.

Mr. Brewster couldn't help smiling. But his reply was firm. "Tomorrow is our Sabbath, children. It is our day to worship and praise God. We will not go ashore or do any work tomorrow."

The children did not ask again. The next morning Richard joined in the worship. He listened closely to Mr. Brewster's sermon.

"We are only a few pilgrims who have come all alone to this far land," Mr. Brewster said. "But our God has kept us safe this far. He will keep us safe through the winter here in the New World. We will have freedom to worship Him."

Land At Last

Monday morning dawned fair and clear. Excitement filled the air.

Francis Billington, who was about twelve, stood beside Richard at the rail. "Is that an Indian I see?" he whispered. He pointed toward shore.

"Francis, you can't see anyone from this far away!" Richard said. But he shivered with excitement at the older boy's words. He just knew that somewhere on that shore there were Indians watching the ship. What would it be like to meet an Indian face to face?

The sounds of people calling to each other broke into Richard's thoughts. He saw women gathering dirty laundry. They would find a place on shore to scrub the clothes. A small boat took the Pilgrims from the *Mayflower* to land. How glad they were to stand on solid ground again!

"The New World," Mistress Brewster breathed. "God has given us a beautiful new world where we can worship Him."

"There are the seagulls!" The little children laughed and clapped their hands. They ran into the middle of a flock of gulls, waving their arms. The birds screeched at the children before flying away.

"Children," Mr. Brewster called, "get some buckets and gather clams and mussels for our supper. Look." He pointed at small holes in the sand. "They are under the sand all over the shore. We won't have to eat stale bread tonight!"

The children raced to see who could be first to find a mussel. Then they raced to fill their buckets.

Suddenly Remember Allerton dropped the pail she was carrying. "What's that?" she cried, pointing to the bay. A stream of water spouted up not far from shore.

"Look out in the bay," cried Wrestling. "Do you see it?"

Slowly a big, black shape rose up out of the water. The men saw it and laughed.

"It's a whale," they said. "Look! Others are coming up for air now."

The children ran to the edge of the water. They had never seen whales this close before. They watched until the whales were gone. Then the children began to fill their buckets again.

The hours passed quickly. All too soon, the children heard Mr. Brewster speak. "Our work is done. It is time to go back to the ship," he called.

"Oh, but Mr. Brewster, we have not seen an Indian yet. Let us stay and see an Indian, please," Richard pleaded.

"Richard, I think you will be seeing an Indian soon enough," Mr. Brewster replied. "We must return to the ship for supper and bed."

Everyone helped to gather the laundry. On the deck the men and children helped to hang it out to dry. Ropes and railings were covered with fresh clean clothes.

After supper Mr. Brewster stood by Richard at the railing. Together they watched seagulls dive for pieces of bread that the children threw to them. "Today has been a special day, Richard," Mr. Brewster said. "This is a good land, a very good land. Our trip was a hard one, but the Lord Jesus brought us safely through it. He will give us what we need here in this New World."

The Boy and the Dike

Far away in the land of Holland, the tulips bloom in bright red, yellow, and orange colors. The dikes hold back the waves of the sea. And the blades of the windmills sing whoosh, whoosh, whoosh as they turn in the wind.

In that far land a tale is told about a boy named Jan who lived down by the dikes. His family owned a small farm along the high-walled dikes.

Jan often walked down the gravel road alongside the dike. It led to his grandmother's house. But that was a long walk away.

He called his grandmother *Oma*, as all good Dutch children do. And she told him long tales as all good Dutch grandmothers do. Her tales were about brave Dutchmen and the things they had done. They were about the dikes that kept the sea from flooding the farms.

Jan loved to listen to Oma's stories. He went to visit her often. One day Mother wrapped up a loaf of fresh brown bread for Jan to give to Oma. Soon he was on his way.

"You may stay overnight if Oma asks you to," Mother called.

Jan skipped happily along the road. His wooden shoes clicked and clacked on the gravel. He stamped along beside the dike while the waves smashed and thrashed on the other side.

Jan splashed through a puddle of water. Then he stopped. It had not rained today. Where could the water have come from? Then he saw a tiny trickle of water coming from the dike. He looked at the tall, thick dike. A tiny hole had begun to grow and the seawater was seeping through it.

"Oh, no!" Jan cried. He knew the little trickle would soon become a flood.

He stuck a stick in it. The water pushed it out.

He stuck a rock in it. The water pushed that out too.

Jan could tell the hole was growing quickly. He put his finger in the stream of water. Ever so slowly it stopped.

Jan looked across the field. No houses were in sight. He looked down the road. No cart rumbled along this late in the day. In fact, the sun had begun to set.

"Help!" Jan called.

No one heard. Jan did not dare leave.
The hole would grow and seawater would
flood all the land for miles. He could never
run quickly enough to get help.

He leaned against the dike and waited.
The sun set. Above him the stars came out
and the moon lit up the fields. Hours
passed. But no one came near.

Jan nibbled on Oma's bread. He remembered the stories she had told about strong
men. They had carried huge rocks to make
the dikes strong. They had built them to

protect the land. They had battled with the sea. Now Jan would fight too. His finger felt as cold as ice, but he would not let the sea win the battle.

At last the long night ended. The sky grew lighter and lighter. A horse pulling a little milk cart rumbled down the road.

"Help!" Jan cried.

The milkman and his son stopped their cart and came running. "What is wrong?" they asked.

"There is a hole in the dike. Quick! Get the men in the village," Jan said.

The milkman left his son to help Jan. Then he galloped off.

While he was gone, Jan and the milkman's son waited. They heard the birds wake up and start their singing. They saw the top of the sun peep over the edge of the fields far away.

Then Oma rode up in her rickety goat cart. The milkman had stopped to give her the news first. She had a soft warm blanket to wrap around Jan.

At last the Dutchmen of the village came running to fix the dike. Jan's father and mother and his brothers and sisters came too.

Jan sat close beside his Oma as they rode home. His eyes drooped with sleep.

"Jan," she whispered, "now I have a new tale to tell—about a brave Dutch boy and the dikes of Holland."

The Old Fisherman

A Song on the Wind

The hot sun shone down on the gray-white sand and on Marty and Ben. Marty sat on her beach blanket reading a book. Ben was putting the finishing touches on his sand castle.

"Look, Marty," he called to his older sister, "I built a castle with towers and everything. And it has that thing around it to hold the water and alligators, whatever you call it."

"A moat," said Marty. "Pretty nice castle, Ben. I hope the ocean doesn't carry it away."

"No, I made the castle too far up on the beach for that." Ben pushed a lump of sand into a spot that was starting to crumble. "The wind might wreck it, though. It's blowing pretty hard today."

The wind blew sounds all around the two children. They heard sounds of seagulls crying. They heard sounds of waves crashing on the sand. Then they heard another sound floating on the wind.

"Fish! Fish! Fish!
I'll grab myself a fish.
I'll cook it just the way I wish.
I'll serve it in a silver dish.
Fish! Fish! Fish!"

The singsong voice drifted over the rocks and sand dunes. "What's that?" Ben asked.

56

"It sounds like a fisherman," Marty replied. She put her book down. "Let's go see."

The two of them trudged across the sand. "I think the sound is coming from the other side of those rocks," said Marty.

They climbed up the rocks and peeked over the edge. Sure enough, an old man sat near the edge of the ocean. It looked as though he had some fish in a pile beside him. The two children were too far away to tell for sure. But they could still hear the singsong voice.

"Fish! Fish! Fish!
Just look at all my fish.
I'll give them to my wife to fry.
She'll bake them in a nice fish pie.
And I'll eat fish until I die.
Fish! Fish! Fish!"

"Fish pie!" Marty and Ben giggled. "He sounds nice!" Ben said. "Let's go meet him."

"No, Ben," Marty reminded him. "We aren't supposed to go near strangers without Daddy or Mother." But she wanted to see more too. So they both climbed on top of the rocks. There they could lean against the rocks and listen to him together.

"Listen!" whispered Ben. "Now he's singing a church song. You hear it?"

"Yes, I hear it," Marty whispered back. "It's 'Amazing Grace.'"

"If he's singing a song from church, that means we can go down and talk to him," Ben said. "Come on!"

"No, Ben!" Marty grabbed her brother by the wrist. "We aren't supposed to go near a stranger alone. Not even if he has on a stovepipe hat and looks like Abraham Lincoln!"

Benjamin Christian

Ben had to laugh at the thought of the old man wearing a stovepipe hat, singing about fish pie. But he knew Marty was right. "Well, then, let's go see if Daddy can come with us. Don't you want to meet that old man too?"

Marty had to admit that she did. The two children scrambled down the rock. They ran through the hot sand to their house. Mr. Billings was putting away his tools from work. He heard the children calling.

"Mother, Daddy!" they both cried together as they ran up the path. "We found an old man on the beach who sings songs about fish and fish pie and church songs, and he looks really nice and can we go meet him?"

With both of them yelling at once, Daddy couldn't understand a word they were saying. He just laughed until they calmed down.

"Now," he said, still chuckling, "let me get the story straight. Did you want to meet someone on the beach? Mother has gone shopping, but I can go with you."

"Yes! Yes!" said the children.

They took turns telling Daddy about the old man. It wasn't long at all before the three of them were trudging through the sand. Mr. Billings walked in the middle with one child holding each hand. Both of them were pulling him to make him go faster.

61

"I hope he hasn't gone," Ben said.

"He hasn't," Marty said. "Listen, I hear him singing! Oh, I wish Mother hadn't left. I want her to meet him too."

The same voice still floated above the sound of the waves. It was singing "Jesus, Saviour, Pilot Me."

"That sounds like a voice I've heard before," Daddy said.

The waves crashed loudly on the beach. But the old man must have heard them coming. He looked around even before they were very near.

Ben and Marty looked at him with interest. He wore a red shirt and faded old blue jeans. The fish he had been singing about were in a bucket beside him. But now the children saw the things they couldn't see before. His wrinkled skin was tanned a dark brown from being in the sun. He had white eyebrows and white hair tucked under a white cap.

But what twinkly gray eyes peered out from under those eyebrows!

"Sir," said Daddy, "I'm Robert Billings. I remember you. You're Mr. Christian, aren't you?"

The old man nodded and smiled. He whipped off his white cap and bowed before his three visitors. "Benjamin Christian is my name. I was born a Christian twice, the first time sixty-seven years ago, and the second time forty-one years ago when I was saved." When he looked up, the children saw that his eyes were twinkling more than ever.

"You have the same name I do!" Ben exclaimed. "Except I'm not Benjamin Christian, I'm Benjamin Billings."

"Benjamin is a fine name to have," Mr. Christian said. "A fine Bible name."

A Sailor's Testimony

"Children," Daddy said, "Mr. Christian gave his testimony at church only a few weeks ago. He sang some songs for us too."

"I don't remember seeing him," said Ben.

"That's because we go to children's church, Ben," whispered Marty. "That's why we didn't see him."

"Well, Mr. Christian," said Ben, "I was born seven years ago. But I was born a Christian two years ago. Won't you tell us your testimony now, since we missed it?"

"Why surely, young man and little lady. That is, if your daddy doesn't mind hearing it again."

"I'd enjoy it very much," said Daddy.

"The wind was whipping more wildly than this on that day when I left home forty-nine years ago," Mr. Christian began. "I was a wicked boy. I wanted to get away from home and my mother's teaching. She was a Christian—twice. I had never been born again, and I didn't want to be."

Marty and Ben sat in the sand and listened closely as Mr. Christian continued.

"I left my village with all my things packed into a bag. I went to a seaport. Ships were docked all up and down the coast. People were everywhere trading and selling, talking loudly, so loudly you couldn't even hear the seagulls crying.

"I got on a ship that was going far away. That was just what I wanted to do. I became a sailor.

"Oh, little friends, I'm ashamed to say it. But I was the wildest and wickedest sailor on the ship. The other men sometimes made fun of me for my name.

"'Benjamin Christian!' they would yell at me. 'You're the worst Christian I've ever seen!'

"That only made me want to be all the more wicked. I wanted to forget everything my mother had tried to teach me. Oh, what a sinner I was!"

Mr. Christian stopped, listening to the crashing waves. "For years I went on like this. Sometimes I remembered the verses my mother had taught me. But I always put them out of my mind. I wanted to run away from God.

"But thank the Lord, He loved me too much to let me run away from Him. One night there was a storm at sea. Have you ever been through a storm on the beach?" Mr. Christian looked at Ben and Marty.

"Oh, yes!" Marty said. "Storms are loud and awful. They scare me!"

"Well, little lady, a storm at sea would scare you ten times worse. The sky was black with thunderclouds. The waves crashed against the ship. They crashed so hard that we were afraid the ship would be broken to bits. Even the sailors who had been sailing the seas all their lives were afraid in this storm.

"During those dark hours it seemed as if
I remembered all the bad things I had ever
done. It seemed as if all the things my
mother had taught me came back to my
mind. For the first time in many years, I
bowed my head and prayed. I prayed, 'Oh,
Lord, I'm a worthless sinner, and I know
it. Please forgive me of my sins and save
me. If You will keep me safe through this
storm, I'll live the rest of my life for
You.' "

70

Amazing Grace

Mr. Christian looked at Ben and Marty as he finished his story. "Do you know what happened? God did forgive me of my sins and save me. And He kept me safe through that storm. And I did what I promised I would do. I obeyed God. My life was never the same after that. The other sailors saw that I had become a *real* Christian, a Christian in life, not only in my name. And some of them were saved too. I went home to my mother to thank her for praying for me.

"That sounds exciting," said Ben. "But I'm glad I was never in a storm like that."

"Yes, you should be glad," Mr. Christian agreed. "And be glad you were saved when you were young. Now you can live your entire life for the Lord. You don't have to waste any of it."

"May we come to visit you sometimes when you are here on the beach?" Marty asked.

"Why, yes. In fact, I would like to have all of your family visit me in my home tomorrow. I'll show you some of the things I collected while I was a sailor."

"Oh, boy!" both children exclaimed. "May we, Daddy?"

"Well, I suppose so," Daddy answered. "That would be very nice, Mr. Christian."

"Will we get to have some fish pie?" Ben grinned.

"Oh, so you heard my song, did you?"
Mr. Christian's eyes twinkled merrily. "Why,
I wouldn't ever let you leave my house
without giving you some fish pie!"

He threw back his head and sang,

"Fish! Fish! Fish!
My wife will cook our fish.
A fishy pie, a fishy cake.
Just look at all the things she'll bake!
You'll get a fishy stomachache
From fish, fish, fish!"

Marty and Ben laughed and laughed at this new verse to the song. Daddy chuckled too.

But then Mr. Christian's face got thoughtful. "Children," he said, "I'm glad you like that song. But I have a story to tell you about a sailor who was in a storm at sea just like the one I was in. He was saved too, just like me. His name was John Newton."

"John Newton," murmured Ben. "I don't think I've ever met him."

Mr. Christian smiled. "That's because he lived a long time ago, Ben. But he wrote the beautiful words to a song that you may know. It has become a very special song to me, because he was saved pretty much the same way I was. The name of the song is 'Amazing Grace.'"

"'Amazing Grace'!" Marty exclaimed. "I heard you singing that a little while ago!"

"So did I," said Ben. "I think it's going to be my favorite song now too."

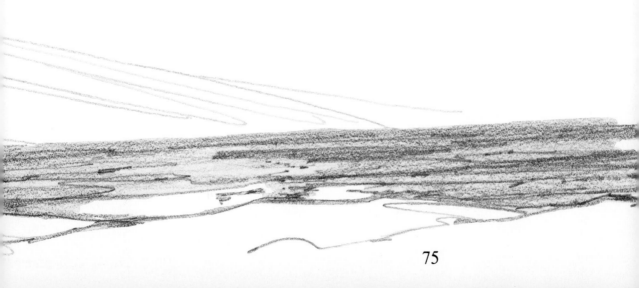

"Let's all sing it now, and thank God for saving us," Mr. Christian said.

They all looked out far over the ocean to the place where the water meets the sky. Even the seagulls were quiet as the four voices were carried on the wind over the rocks and sand dunes.

"Amazing grace!
How sweet the sound,
That saved a wretch like me!
I once was lost,
But now am found,
Was blind, but now I see."

The Picnic

We brought a rug for sitting on,
Our lunch was in a box.
The sand was warm. We didn't wear
Hats or Shoes or Socks.

Waves came curling up the beach.
We waded. It was fun.
Our sandwiches were different kinds.
I dropped my jelly one.

by Dorothy Aldis

77

Fishers of Men

(taken from John 21:1-14)

The Empty Net

Jesus had risen from the dead! The disciples had seen Him with their own eyes. Now He was gone, but He had told them to wait for Him.

Waiting was not easy. The days seemed long. The men had been fishermen before Christ had called them to be His disciples. They loved the sea and the roaring waves. But they had left everything to follow Christ.

They wanted to be busy again. One afternoon Peter had an idea. "I'm going fishing," he said to the others.

Eight or nine of the others went with him. Quickly they gathered their net and left the village. They found a boat and pushed it into the sea.

Before long the men had sailed a short way from shore. They put weights on their net and let it slip into the water.

The waves rippled and rocked the boat.

"Have we caught anything?" Peter asked.

Thomas began pulling in the net. John pulled on the other end. Soon it lay in a heap on the deck. Not one fish wiggled in the tangled ropes. The net was empty.

They dropped it over the side again.

"It's getting dark," Nathanael said. "The fish should start swimming into our net now."

They waited and waited. Some of the men fell asleep. The stars twinkled and the moon lit up the water.

At last they pulled in the net again. But it was as empty as before.

"I'm hungry," Thomas said.

"We can't eat until we catch some fish," Peter said. "Put the net back into the water."

The stars faded as the sun sent its first rays over the sea. The night had passed. The disciples pulled up the net. They were sure it would be full of great big fish this time.

Up came the net. All of the men helped to pull it in. It dripped large puddles of water onto the deck, but there were no fish.

The boat had drifted close to shore. The disciples saw a little fire. A man stood by it looking out at their boat.

"Have you any fish?" he called.

"No," they called back.

The man stepped closer to the water.

"Do you know who he is?" one of the disciples asked.

"No," the others answered.

"He must want some fish to eat this morning," Peter said.

The man on the shore called to them again. "Cast the net on the right side of the boat, and you will find fish."

They hauled the net to the other side.

"Careful or you will break it," Peter said.

"Maybe we should just go home. We have not caught anything all night. We won't catch anything now," Thomas said.

"Let's try one more time. We have the net over here already," Peter answered.

Quickly they threw the net over the side and watched it sink beneath the waves.

"I think we have caught something," Peter said. "Pull it in."

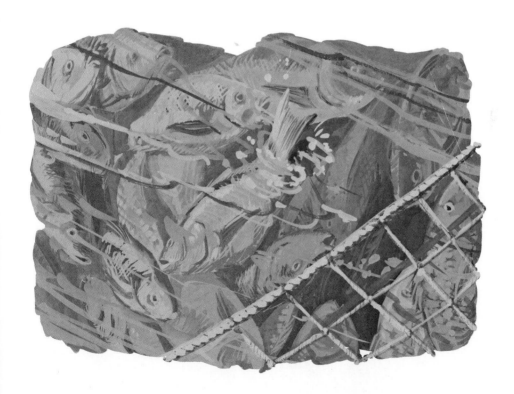

Follow Me

Two of the disciples tugged at the net. It wouldn't move. The others joined them. Slowly the net rose to the top. The scales of the fish in it glistened like silver treasure.

"Look!" James shouted.

"The net is too full," Nathanael said. "It is going to break."

"Can we get it into the boat?" another asked.

"No, we had better drag it to shore," Thomas said. The full net bumped against the side of the boat.

John shaded his eyes and peered at the shore. The man still stood there. The other disciples turned to John. "It is the Lord!" John said.

Before anyone else could speak, Peter grabbed his fisherman's coat and jumped into the sea. He swam quickly to shore. Finally his feet touched the sandy bottom, and he ran up the beach.

The other disciples dragged the net along to the shore. Then they too jumped over the side and ran up the beach.

Jesus had a small fire with fish cooking on it for them. He had bread for them too.

"Bring the fish which you have now caught," He said to them.

Peter hurried to the boat and hauled in the net. He counted one hundred fifty-three fish in it. That was more than he had ever caught in one net!

"The net didn't break," he said to the others.

They shook their heads. They couldn't believe it had held so many.

Then Jesus called them to eat. He gave fish and bread to each of them.

The disciples ate the food quickly. They had been very hungry, and it tasted good.

After the men were done, Jesus spoke to them. They listened to every word He said. The disciples wanted to remember what He told them.

After the Lord had left them, the disciples put up their fishing net. They left the boat.

Soon the disciples were ready to go from town to town telling about the Lord Jesus.

They would not fish for fish anymore. Now they would fish only for men. The disciples would use the gospel to bring others to the Lord.

All of the disciples remembered the words Christ had said to them when He first called them. And at last they understood.

"Follow me, and I will make you fishers of men."

Matthew 4:19b

New Friends

Kristy and Juanita

It was Juanita's first day of school in America. She sat at her desk and watched the boys and girls. They laughed and talked quietly all around her. Juanita sighed. She could understand only a little English. She knew the American children would not understand her Spanish.

"Hi!" said a pretty girl with curly red hair.

Juanita knew that word. "Hi!" she said, smiling.

The girl began talking. Juanita shook her head. "I speak no English," she said.

The girl looked puzzled.

Just then Mr. Mullins called the class to order. They all stood to say the pledge to the American flag. Juanita stood up tall and proud with her hand over her heart. She could not say the pledge yet, but America was her new country. She was glad to go to school and planned to work hard to learn English.

The class said the pledges to the Christian flag and to the Bible. Then Mr. Mullins prayed. Juanita silently thanked God for her new Christian school.

Mr. Mullins spoke to the class in English. He called Juanita's name and held up some books and supplies for her. Juanita hurried to the front of the class to pick them up. As she carried them to her desk, the girl with the curly red hair smiled at her. Then the class began their work.

For a little while Juanita looked at the bright pictures in her schoolbooks. Then Mr. Mullins came to her desk. He handed Juanita a paper and said something to the redheaded girl. She pulled her chair up next to Juanita's.

"Juanita," Mr. Mullins said, "this is Kristy."

"Kristy?" Juanita asked, looking at the girl.

"Yes, my name is Kristy," the girl said. She showed Juanita the math work the class was doing. Soon Juanita was busy working too.

She quickly finished all the problems on her paper. "Done," she said.

"Good!" Kristy exclaimed.

Juanita nodded. "Sí," she said.

Kristy and Juanita worked together the rest of the morning.

"It is time for lunch," Kristy said at last.

"Time? Lunch?" Juanita repeated.

"Sí!" Kristy pretended to eat a sandwich.

Juanita laughed. She understood that. She picked up her lunch box and followed Kristy.

The two girls washed their hands with soap and water at the sink and then went to the lunchroom.

That afternoon Mr. Mullins passed music books to the class. "Our school program is only two weeks away," he said. "We have learned many of the songs, but we have a lot of work to do."

Juanita enjoyed listening as the class sang. She knew how to sing some of the songs in Spanish. Mr. Mullins let her sing one to the class.

"Would you like to sing Juanita's song in the program?" Mr. Mullins asked.

"Yes, sir!" was the answer.

Next they worked on Bible verses. Mr. Mullins wrote a verse for Juanita to learn.

He said the verse very slowly.

Juanita looked at the strange English words.

Mr. Mullins said it once again, a little at a time. Juanita repeated it, but she did not think she would ever remember all the words.

"I will help you," Kristy said.

Another Friend

Every day Kristy helped Juanita with her verse. Juanita's mother had explained the verse in Spanish and Juanita enjoyed saying it in Spanish too.

One night Kristy went to dinner at Juanita's house. Juanita's mother made tacos. Juanita showed Kristy how to fill the cornmeal taco shell. She put in meat, beans, cheese, and tomato sauce. Kristy ate two tacos.

Juanita ate her taco with hot sauce. Kristy tasted a little bit of the sauce, but it burned her mouth.

Juanita's mother made something special called *flan*. It tasted like sweet pudding covered with caramel. Kristy ate a piece. Then she was full.

After dinner Juanita tried to say her verse to Kristy. "Romans 5:8. 'But God commendeth his love toward us in that,—in that,—in that . . . ,'" she stumbled.

"'While we were yet sinners,'" Kristy said.

"'While we were yet sinners,'" Juanita repeated.

"'Christ died for us,'" said Kristy.

They finished just before Kristy's father came to take her home. "Good night, Juanita," Kristy said.

Juanita waved from the doorway. Maybe she would know her verse tomorrow.

On Saturday Juanita played in the park. "Romans 5:8. 'But God commendeth his love toward us,'" she said as the swing went up. "Romans 5:8," she repeated as the swing came down.

A girl on the swing next to her listened to the words.

"What is Romans 5:8?" she asked.

Juanita gulped. Did the girl want her to say the Bible verse? Maybe she did not know that Christ had died for her sins. Juanita tried hard to remember her verse. She must be able to say it.

"'But God commendeth his love toward us in that, while we were yet sinners, Christ died for us,'" Juanita said. She had remembered every word!

"Christ died for me?" the girl asked.

"Sí," Juanita said. She thought of all the English words she had learned. Could she explain to the girl that Christ would forgive her sins?

"Juanita!" a voice called.

Juanita turned around. "Kristy!" she said.

Kristy skipped up to the swings. "Tell Romans 5:8," Juanita said, pointing to the other girl.

As Kristy explained the Bible verse, Juanita listened carefully. She wanted to know how to tell others about Jesus, in English.

Kristy told the girl about the program at school.

"I promise to come to your school program," the girl said. "Thank you for telling me about it."

The days passed quickly. Every day Kristy and Juanita prayed for the girl they had met in the park. Every day Juanita said her verse to Kristy.

The night of the program, Juanita's class marched out proudly. They sang the English songs, and then they sang Juanita's Spanish song.

The time came to say the Bible verses. Juanita looked at the crowd. The girl from the park was sitting in the front row! She smiled at Juanita.

"Romans 5:8 . . . ," Juanita began. Then she said the verse perfectly.

After the program Juanita ran to find Kristy. Very carefully she said each English word.

"Thank you for helping me, Kristy. You are a kind friend."

Then together the two girls went to find their new friend from the park.

Bread from Heaven

(a true story)

The Battlefield

Dwight Moody knelt beside the wounded soldier and felt his wrist. He saw the man's lips move, but he could not hear above the rattle of the passing wagons. Leaning closer, he could barely make out the words.

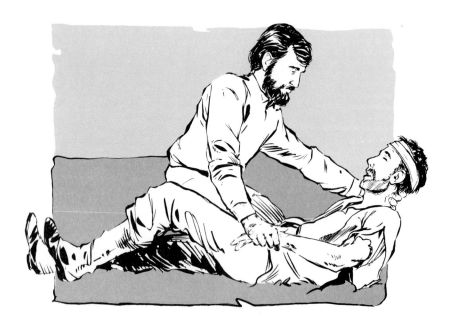

"Pray for me, Mr. Moody," the man whispered.

"What's your name, son?"

"Billy, sir," was the faint answer.

"Before we pray, Billy, let me tell you what God says about eternal life." Mr. Moody shared some verses with the young soldier and told him how to be saved.

"Would you like to know Jesus as your Saviour, Billy?"

"Yes, sir," Billy replied.

"Then let's pray," Mr. Moody said.

After Billy had trusted Jesus as his Saviour, he lay back, smiling peacefully.

The general galloped past on his horse. He stopped and came back when he saw Mr. Moody.

"Mr. Moody," the general said, "will you and your friends take charge of the wounded? Our men are already fighting down the road. We have no time to spare. We must join them."

"We are not doctors," said Mr. Moody. "But by God's grace we will do what we can."

"By God's grace it will have to be," the general said. Leaning over, he shook Mr. Moody's hand. "We'll be back as soon as we can."

He galloped on with the soldiers.

Mr. Moody watched as the last wagon rumbled down the dirt road. The only sound on the battlefield was the moaning of the wounded soldiers.

Mr. Moody called his friends together. "We came to give the gospel to these soldiers," he said. "But now God asks us to do more. I know we are not doctors, but we can be of some help. Only God knows when the army can return. Do what you can for the wounded and pray with them."

A man nearby pushed himself up on one elbow. He called, "Water! Please, water!"

"There's a stream a short walk away," Mr. Moody told his friends. "Take as many canteens as you can carry. I will do what I can until you return."

The young men gathered up the canteens and headed for the stream. Mr. Moody rolled up his sleeves and began to work. He wrapped wounds with clean cloth and prayed with each soldier.

The Prayer Meeting

Soon Mr. Moody's friends returned with full canteens. Quickly they moved among the soldiers, giving them water. As they helped the thirsty soldiers drink, they told them about God's love for them. Many soldiers trusted Christ as their Saviour that long afternoon.

The sun began to set behind the hills. The friends gathered to talk.

"What about food?" asked one.

"Yes, it has been hours since they have eaten," replied another.

"Let's see what we can find in the knapsacks," Mr. Moody said. "Perhaps the soldiers carried enough rations to feed at least this many."

The men emptied the knapsacks and piled the rations on a sheet of canvas in front of Mr. Moody. He shook his head slowly. "There is not enough food for everyone," he said. "The weak and wounded must have food soon or they will die."

The men looked at each other. The nearest village was miles away.

"I guess I could walk to the village," suggested one of the men.

"No," Mr. Moody said, "every man is needed to help the wounded."

Mr. Moody knelt on the ground beside the sheet of canvas. The other men knelt beside him and began to pray. They asked God to send bread, but they had no idea how their prayer would be answered.

After they had prayed, Mr. Moody stood up. "Now, let's leave the problem of food with God," he said.

The men went back to work. All through the night, they cared for the soldiers. Tired and still hungry, they welcomed the first light of dawn. Then in the stillness they heard the sound of a wagon.

"Is the army coming back?" someone asked.

They all peered through the morning mist. A large wagon rumbled up the road and stopped in front of them. It was filled to the top with loaves of bread!

The driver jumped down from the wagon seat. "Who's in charge here?" he asked.

"I am," replied Mr. Moody. He held out his hand. "I'm Dwight Moody."

The driver shook his hand. "Glad to meet you, Dr. Moody. I'm Mr. Stevens."

Mr. Moody smiled. "We're not doctors, sir, only friends who wanted to help the soldiers."

"I want to help too," said the driver. "I saw the army go past last night. When I went to bed, I couldn't sleep. All I could think about was the wounded soldiers left behind. I woke my wife and told her that we must take food to the wounded soldiers. We had only a little bread in the house.

"While Mrs. Stevens was busy baking more, I hitched up the wagon. I drove from Martin Street all the way to the church on South Avenue, waking up my neighbors. They gave me all the bread in their houses.

"At last my wagon was full. When I got home, my wife's bread was done. I piled her bread on top. I drove away feeling as though the Lord Himself was sending me."

Tears came to Mr. Moody's eyes. "Mr. Stevens, the Lord did send you. Let us give thanks for His faithfulness."

Heads bowed as Mr. Moody prayed, thanking the Lord for the bread. When he finished, he smiled at the men. "Now let's unload the bread from heaven and feed the soldiers!"

The Farmer and the Donkey

Cast

Narrator

Farmer

Son

Glum, the donkey

Baker

Blacksmith

Tailor

Tailor's Wife

Miller

Townsfolk

Storekeeper

Off To Town

Narrator: Once upon a time there lived an old farmer, his son, and their gray-eared donkey named Glum. Now the old farmer worked hard on his farm, and his son almost always helped him. The old farmer had only one problem. He always tried to take everyone's advice. Then, one day . . .

Farmer: Time for us to leave, son. Hi-ho, we must hurry along to town to sell the donkey.

Son: Coming, Father. I'll fetch Glum's rope.

Glum: Hee-haw. Hee-haw.

Farmer: The farm will be very quiet without Glum to wake us up every morning with his braying.

Son: I will miss him.

Glum: Hee-haw. Hee-haw.

Narrator: Soon the old farmer had bolted the door and had set off down the dirt road with his son and Glum, the donkey. Whom should they meet but their friend the baker, pushing his cart of rolls and sweetcakes.

Baker: Hello there! What's this? A fine donkey trotting merrily along, and you two scurrying along to keep up. One of you should ride him!

Farmer: That is good advice, friend baker. Climb up, son, and we'll be on our way to town to sell our donkey.

Baker: Such a fine donkey should bring a good price—especially with those long gray ears he has.

Glum: Hee-haw. Hee-haw.

Narrator: So the two set off for the town again with Glum, the donkey, carrying the farmer's son, who bobbed up and down with each step. The farmer marched along in front of them.

Son: Father, here comes the blacksmith. He must be on his way home from town.

Blacksmith: Good morning, friend farmer. What's this? Your son rides while you walk? People will think he is lazy.

Farmer: You are right. Jump down, son. Let me ride.

Blacksmith: Yes, let your son's strong legs trot along while you rest your tired bones.

Farmer: Thank you, kind blacksmith. My friends always have such helpful advice. Now we must be off to town to sell this donkey.

Blacksmith: Glad I could help. You have a fine-looking donkey. What beautiful, long, gray ears he has!

Glum: Hee-haw. Hee-haw.

Narrator: Again the two set off. This time the farmer rode Glum, bouncing and jouncing at every step. The farmer's son trotted along beside them.

You Cannot Please Everyone

Narrator: An hour later the farmer and his son reached the town. They trotted by the tailor's house as the tailor and his wife sat on their porch.

Tailor's Wife: Tut, tut, and look at that; the farmer rides along while his little boy has to run as best he can to keep up. For shame!

Farmer: Well, well. What can I do?

Tailor: Why, your fine donkey could surely carry both of you!

Farmer: Oh, what good advice. I should have thought of it myself. Thank you, kind tailor.

Son: Should I climb up behind you, Father?

Farmer: Yes, come along. With both of us riding, we will reach the market place in no time at all.

Narrator: The farmer and his son again set off, bouncing up and down and back and forth as Glum wobbled down the street. Before long the miller met them with his sack of wheat slung over his arm.

Miller: What's this? Such a sad donkey. I would never wish to carry such a heavy load as he has been carrying. He looks like he might fall over and die. His long gray ears are drooping so low they almost reach the ground.

Farmer: Well, I guess this is a heavy load for Glum.

Miller: Indeed! You should carry him!

Farmer: We will. Son, find a long pole. We can tie Glum to it with his rope and carry him between us.

Son: Yes, sir. Here's one by the street.

Miller: Your donkey's long gray ears have perked up already.

Farmer: Good. We are taking him to the market place to sell him. No one will pay for him if he is worn out from carrying us. Thank you for the good advice.

Miller: You're welcome! Take care of your donkey.

Narrator: At last the two set off again with Glum's feet tied to a pole. The farmer carried one end of the pole and his son carried the other end. They shuffled along slowly till they reached the cobblestone streets of the market place.

Townsfolk: Look, look! What's this?

Storekeeper: A man and a boy are carrying a donkey!

Townsfolk: What a strange sight!

Storekeeper: I can't believe anyone would do something so foolish.

Townsfolk: Oh, ho-ho-ho-ho-ha-ha-ha! How foolish! How silly!

Glum: Hee-haw. Hee-haw.

Farmer: Hush, hush! You're frightening my donkey.

Glum: Hee-Haw! HEE-HAW! HEE-HAW!

Narrator: At that Glum pulled and kicked till his rope broke and the pole snapped in two. He rolled over and began to run.

Glum: HEE-HAW! HEE-HAW!

118

Farmer: Quick! Catch him!

Son: (panting) Stop him! He's running away!

Townsfolk: There he goes! All you can see are his long gray ears.

Farmer: Alas, my donkey is gone. I foolishly took bad advice.

Son: Now we cannot ride, carry, or even sell Glum.

Farmer: I have learned my lesson too late. In trying to please everyone, I have pleased no one.

As to the Lord

"The cookies are ready!" Mother came out of the kitchen with a plate full of cookies, still warm from the oven.

Rachel, Phil, and Julie looked up from their homework. "Thank you, Mother!" they said.

"I made some bread today too. It will be cool enough to eat at supper."

This was Friday, Mother's baking day, and she had been baking for hours. Now it was time to wash the dishes. But the ringing telephone stopped Mother from her work. When she hung up, there was a look of happiness mixed with concern on her face.

"Children, your grandmother and grandfather are coming!"

"They are?" the three shouted at once. "When?"

"They're at the airport right now and want me to pick them up!" Mother looked around at the jumbled schoolbooks and toys. "Oh, this house is a mess. I'll have to pick up Dad from work on the way back from the airport. I'll be gone about two hours. Please put away your books and toys before I get back." And with a quick good-bye, she was gone.

After Mother left, Julie stood thinking for a moment about Grandma and Grandpa's visit. "I have an idea," she exclaimed suddenly. "Remember Colossians 3:23? Mother taught it to us last week."

"I remember," said Phil. "It's 'And whatsoever ye do, do it heartily, as to the Lord, and not unto men.' "

"Yes!" said Julie. "So let's do all our work and then do the rest of the housework too. We can be finished before Mother gets back."

"That's a good idea, Julie," said Rachel. "We want the house looking especially nice for Grandma and Grandpa when they come. But we'll have to work fast."

So the three worked harder and faster than they ever had before. Schoolbooks were stacked up, photograph albums were put back on the shelves, and toys and games were put away.

"Finished!" they sighed together, as they sat down to rest.

"Now I think I know what it means to do things heartily," gasped Julie. "I'm worn out!"

"But we still have to clean up the kitchen, sweep the carport, vacuum the living room, and dust," Rachel said. "Since I'm the oldest, I'd better put away things in the kitchen. What do you two want to do?"

"I'll vacuum," said Phil. "That's kind of fun anyway."

"I'll dust," Julie said. "I'm good at that. I guess I can sweep too."

"And when I'm finished, I'll help you put things away in the kitchen," Phil said to Rachel.

Once again the house hummed with busy workers.

Before long the work was all done, and the three plopped down on the couch again. Just at that instant Mother and Dad walked in the door with two smiling people behind them.

"Grandma and Grandpa!" Happy shouts filled the room as Grandma and Grandpa were covered with hugs and kisses.

"I'm really sorry for the way the house looks, Grandma," Mother said, "but I just didn't have time—"

"Why, what are you talking about?" Grandma exclaimed. "It's neat as a pin."

Mother looked all around and saw that Grandma was right. Even the kitchen was clean. "Children, did you do all this?" she asked. Three beaming faces gave her the answer. "What thoughtful children!" she said as she hugged them.

"We were thinking of Colossians 3:23," said Julie. "Remember, you taught it to us, Mother."

"This calls for a special treat," Dad said. "We'll have homemade ice cream tonight!"

"Oh, boy!" Rachel, Phil, and Julie shouted with joy. "Grandma and Grandpa and homemade ice cream! What a day!"

The Little Maid

(taken from II Kings 5)

Captain Naaman, the Leper

The little maid passed Captain Naaman's room. He had a dreadful illness called leprosy. Large sores that would not heal had spread over his skin. All the doctors in Syria did not know how to make him well.

The little maid was busy all afternoon helping her mistress, but her mistress did not say a word. Once the little maid found her crying in the garden.

"Oh, Mistress, do not weep," she said, bringing her a cool cloth to wipe away her tears.

Her mistress shook her head. "Captain Naaman is very ill," she said.

Tears came to the little maid's eyes. "Will he get better?" she asked.

"No," her mistress answered, "Captain Naaman will never fight in great battles again. He will never get better."

"I wish I could help him," the little maid said. "If only my master would go to the prophet Elisha in my home country. Elisha could heal him."

Just then a servant walked past the garden and heard them talking.

"What did you say, child?" he asked.

"I heard of many great works that Elisha did when I lived near him. He is a prophet of the one true God," she said.

The servant hurried on his way, but he did not forget the girl's words.

"Master," he said, kneeling by Naaman's bedside. "May we take you to Elisha? Your wife's little maid says that he can heal you. You can be well again!"

"Elisha?" Naaman asked.

"Yes, he is a prophet of God. The little maid is sure he can heal you," the servant said.

"Then we will leave tomorrow," said Naaman.

Naaman's servants packed silver, gold, and beautiful clothes to pay Elisha. Then Naaman climbed into the chariot.

Days passed as they traveled on the hot, dusty roads. The horses trotted mile after mile, carrying Captain Naaman to Elisha.

As his chariot bumped along, Naaman thought about the prophet of God. Would Elisha stand in front of Naaman and call loudly to God to heal him? Would he strike the sores with his hand? Would the sores just disappear? Could the little maid's God heal him?

At last Captain Naaman arrived in Elisha's city. His chariot came to a stop in front of Elisha's door.

Captain Naaman stepped down from the chariot.

Inside the house Elisha spoke quietly to his servant. The servant hurried to the door. He opened the door before Naaman could knock.

"Naaman," the servant said, "Elisha sent me to tell you to go and wash in the Jordan River seven times, and your skin will be clean. You will be made well."

"Wash in the Jordan seven times?" Naaman said in an angry voice.

Naaman turned to his servants. "I thought Elisha would at least come out to talk to me. He just sent his servant to tell me to wash in the dirty Jordan River. I can go to the clean rivers at home to wash!" He stomped away, muttering to himself. Into his chariot he climbed.

"Master," one servant said, "will you go to the Jordan River?"

Captain Naaman frowned. "No! Take me home!" he ordered.

Naaman's servants turned sadly back to the chariots. Their master would never be made well. Then one servant ran up to Captain Naaman.

"Master," he said, "if Elisha had asked you to do something hard, would you have done it?"

Another servant joined the first. "Yes, Master, if Elisha had asked you to do a great thing, you would have done it. Can't you do this easy thing?"

"We want you to be made well, Master," the servants said.

Naaman looked at his faithful servants. "Yes," he said. "You're right. Take me to the Jordan River."

In the Jordan River

Naaman watched the trees by the roadside and thought about Elisha. Could Elisha and the little maid's God heal him? If He could, then He would be greater than all the doctors Captain Naaman had seen. They had not been able to heal him. If the little maid's God could heal him, then Naaman would know that He was the one true and living God.

At last they could see the Jordan River.
As the chariot stopped, Naaman saw the
muddy water lap the riverbank. He did not
want to go into the muddy water. But his
servants were waiting to help him from the
chariot, and he had to keep his word.

The servants stood on the bank. Captain Naaman stepped into the river. The water was warm, but it was so muddy he could not see his toes as they squished in the mud. He waded in until the water reached his waist.

Each servant held his breath. Would Naaman's leprosy be gone?

Naaman dunked under the water. The servants looked closely at him. The leprosy was still there.

Down Naaman dunked again. But the sores did not even begin to heal.

Again the third time he dunked himself. Four, five, six times the muddy water closed above his head. One more time would be seven.

Captain Naaman dipped his hands and arms under the water; then he dunked his head under. The servants leaned out over the river to watch Naaman come up.

Slowly, slowly Naaman stood up. He shook the muddy water out of his eyes and looked at his hands and arms.

"Has the little maid's God healed you?" the servants called.

"Yes!" Captain Naaman shouted. "I am well! My skin is as clean as can be!"

The servants almost tripped over each other as they joyfully helped Captain Naaman out of the water.

Every sore was gone. Captain Naaman could never again be called a leper. Quickly Naaman rode back to find Elisha.

"Now I know your God is the true and living God," Naaman said to Elisha. "He is the only God. I will trust in Him."

Naaman called his servants. They held up the riches Naaman had brought. "Take these, Elisha, in payment," Naaman said.

Elisha shook his head. "No, God made you well, Naaman. I cannot take these things."

Naaman turned to leave. "I will always worship the true God. Thank you, Elisha."

Days later Naaman arrived at home. "Captain Naaman is home!" the servants shouted.

The little maid ran outside with her mistress.

Captain Naaman stepped down from the chariot. He showed them his clean skin, glowing with health.

"The little maid's God healed me of my leprosy," he said. "He is the only true God."

Just Mouse

A Noise at the Door

In the back of an old brown house in a tiny hole under a rotten board there lived a mouse. He was an old gray mouse with trembly whiskers and a long gray tail. He lived alone and talked to no one but himself. Sometimes he muttered, "I like the quiet. I like living alone. I don't want to help anybody. I don't want anybody helping me. I never want to see anybody else." And so he lived, waking up alone and going to bed alone, never seeing anyone.

138

One day Mouse lay curled up in his chair, reading. The thunder crashed, the wind howled, and the rain battered against the window. "It's good to have a book to read on such a stormy afternoon," he muttered. "And it's very good to be alone."

He had not been reading long when a scurrying mouse-like sound startled him. "I never hear noises like that unless I make them," he said. "I wonder what it could be."

Taking his old brown cane, he left his hole and peered around the empty house. There, not far from his doorway, he saw a wet little mouse lying very still.

"Humph. He must have fainted." Mouse turned to go back into his hole. "I don't want to help anybody, and I don't want anybody helping me." He stopped. The mouse was very little, and he looked so weak and hungry.

"I guess I could just help him dry off." Mouse shrugged. "And maybe I could give him some cheese."

After only a few moments in the dry, warm hole, the little mouse woke up enough to eat some cheese. "Oh, thank you, sir," he said. "You're a kind mouse. What is your name?"

"Just Mouse," answered Mouse. "Nobody has ever called me anything but Mouse."

"I'm Nipsy," said the small mouse. "I came looking for help for my two brothers. They're caught in a mousetrap. Will you come and help me rescue them?"

Mouse's whiskers trembled. "I don't want to help anybody. . . ." He stopped when he saw a big tear roll down Nipsy's face.

"Just this once," Mouse said slowly. "And then you really must go away and leave me alone."

"Oh, thank you! Thank you!" Nipsy scampered around the room. Mouse picked up his old brown cane and followed Nipsy out of the house and down the trail. "At least the storm has stopped," he muttered.

"They're in a house over that hill," Nipsy
said as he pointed.

"Huh," grunted Mouse. He didn't like
this idea of helping. He only liked being
alone.

"There they are!" Nipsy said. "Hold on!
We're going to save you!" he called.

Mouse looked through the cellar window
to see two frightened little mice comforting
each other in the corner of a cage.

Mouse to the Rescue

Mouse thought about the problem for a moment.

"Maybe I can do something with my cane." Mouse led the way into the room through a crack in the wall. Being careful not to get too close to the trap, he wedged his cane under the cage. Together Mouse and Nipsy pried up the cage. Two little mice scrambled out.

"Oh, thank you! Thank you for saving us!" They scampered around and around, squeaking joyfully. "Who are you?"

"I'm Mouse," said Mouse. "Just Mouse."

"I'm Dipsy," said one mouse.

"I'm Flipsy," said the other.

Mouse grunted. "You three get along home now and stay out of trouble!" He turned to leave. But Nipsy, Dipsy, and Flipsy scampered down the road beside him. Before Mouse could say anything else to them, Dipsy squealed, "Look!"

There against a wall a big black cat had cornered two little frightened mice. "We must rescue them!" cried Flipsy. "But how?"

"I don't want to help. . . ," Mouse began. But he thought about the big black cat eating up the two wee, little mice. He shuddered. Then his mind worked quickly.

"You three little ones run to make the cat chase you over here," he said. "Then I'll fix him."

As brave as tigers, Nipsy, Dipsy, and Flipsy ran toward the black cat. "Catch us if you can!" they yelled, and made faces at him.

The black cat yowled and spat. He forgot the two mice he had cornered and jumped toward the three mice brothers.

Quick as a flash, Nipsy, Dipsy, and Flipsy raced toward Mouse. He stood right in the way of the big black cat.

"Take that!" he cried, and poked the cat sharply in the nose three times.

"MeOWWWW!" yowled the cat, and he ran away as fast as he could go. The two little mice were safe.

"Thank you, thank you!" they cried. "We were sure we would never live to see another mouse! Who are you, sir?"

"I'm just Mouse," said Mouse. "Nothing but Mouse."

"I'm Tubsy," said one mouse.

"I'm George," said the other. "We'll go home with you."

"Oh, no," said Mouse. "I like the quiet. I like living alone. I don't want to help anybody, and I don't want anybody helping me."

But when he turned to go to his house,
Nipsy, Dipsy, Flipsy, Tubsy, and George
trailed right along behind him.

"Go away!"

They still followed him.

"I don't want you!"

Still they followed him.

Finally Mouse gave up and said nothing
more.

When he got home, Nipsy, Dipsy, Flipsy,
Tubsy, and George gathered around him.
"We don't think Mouse is a good enough
name for you," said George. "We've decided
to call you Granddaddy Mouse."

For the first time in all his life, Mouse's little nose twitched as he smiled a wee, little smile. "I don't think that's such a bad name." He sat down in his big easy chair.

"Maybe—" Mouse said as Nipsy climbed into his lap. . .

"Maybe—" he smiled as Flipsy, Tubsy, and Dipsy skipped happily about. . .

"Just maybe," he sighed as George kissed him, "helping might be worth something after all."

Have You Seen My Dog?

Where Is Lady?

Pete jumped down the porch steps. He pushed open the gate to the backyard.

"Here, Lady!" he called. He frowned when there was no answering bark. The fenced yard was empty. "That dog is gone again," Pete said to himself. He got his bike out of the shed and pushed it to the front yard. He stopped beside his father.

"Dad, have you seen Lady?" he asked.

"Why no, Pete," said his father. "Is she gone again?"

"Yes, sir," Pete said. "May I go look for her?"

"Yes," Dad answered. "Why don't you ask Allen to help you?"

Pete rode down the street to his friend's house. Allen was outside mowing the lawn.

"Have you seen Lady?" Pete asked.

Allen stopped the mower. "No, not this morning. Is she gone again?" he asked.

Pete nodded. "She has been wandering off since her puppies died. She must be looking for them."

Pete put the mower away while Allen asked his mother if he could help look for Lady.

"My mother said it's okay," Allen said as he rolled his bike out of the shed. "Let's go!"

The two boys pedaled slowly up the street. They didn't see Lady anywhere.

As they turned the corner of Maple Lane and Main Street, they saw a school friend.

"Hello, Henry!" called Pete.

"What are you two doing?" Henry asked.

"We're looking for my dog," Pete replied. "She got out again and we can't find her anywhere."

"Lady? She ran past here early this morning," said Henry.

"Which way did she go?" Allen asked.

"Out that way." Henry pointed toward the lumberyard.

"Thanks, Henry." The two boys pedaled away.

"Here, Lady!" Pete whistled as they rode past the lumberyard. Allen braked suddenly. "There she is!"

"Lady!" Pete yelled. "Come here!"

The boys turned into the lumberyard. They rode in and out of the stacks of lumber. They could not see Lady. They called and whistled but there was no answer.

"What are you kids doing?" A tall man stopped them as they turned a corner. "You can't ride through here. This isn't a playground!"

"We're sorry, sir," replied Pete. "We were just looking for my dog."

The tall man put his hands on his hips and frowned. "A dog?"

"Yes, sir," said Allen. "I thought I saw her go around that corner."

"A big dog?" The man held his hands about knee high. "Red, floppy ears, big brown eyes?"

"That's Lady!" said Allen.

"She went through a broken board in the back fence," the man replied. "There's a vacant lot over there."

"Thank you!" called the boys as they rode away. They pedaled down the side road to the vacant lot.

"Look," said Allen. He pointed to an old shed almost hidden in the weeds.

A muffled bark came from the shed.

"Lady!" cried Pete. He got off his bike and ran the rest of the way to the shed door.

Lady looked up at the boys and wagged her tail. Then she nudged the squirming, furry bodies beside her.

"Puppies! Lady has puppies!" said Allen.

Pete dropped to his knees beside Lady. "Allen, these aren't puppies!"

Lady's New Family

"What are they?" Allen asked as he leaned over. "You must be kidding!" he laughed. "Kittens!"

"Remember when Lady's puppies died?" Pete asked.

"Yes," Allen said slowly. "She wandered around the neighborhood for days looking for them. I guess she must have found the kittens alone and adopted them."

"Something must have happened to their mother," said Pete. "I wonder how this will work out," he said thoughtfully.

"So do I," Allen said.

"Well," Pete said, "we can take the kittens home in our bike baskets. Lady will follow us."

Lady whimpered as the boys put the kittens into the wire baskets. Then she ran alongside the bikes as the boys pedaled home.

"Mom, Dad!" Pete shouted as they turned into the driveway. "Come and see what we have!"

His mother and father came to the kitchen door. Pete and Allen put the kittens on the grass.

"How pretty," said Mrs. Taylor, picking up one of the kittens. "Where did you find them?"

"We didn't find them. Lady did," said Allen.

"Lady found them?" Mr. Taylor raised his eyebrows.

"Yes, sir. They were in an old shed near the lumberyard," said Allen.

"Where was their mother?" asked Mrs. Taylor.

"We don't know," Pete replied. "Lady was taking care of them."

"You mean she adopted them?" asked Mr. Taylor.

"Yes, sir," said Allen.

"I've heard of animals adopting other animals before," said Mr. Taylor. "But it doesn't happen often. Why don't you telephone the newspaper office? This would make a good story."

Mrs. Taylor brought the kittens inside as Pete and Allen raced for the telephone.

By the time the newspaper reporter arrived, the kittens were well used to their new home. He took a picture of Lady licking her kittens. A few days later, Pete proudly showed the newspaper to his classmates.

Almost every day after that, someone would knock at the kitchen door wanting to see Lady and her kittens. Pete enjoyed taking his friends to meet Lady. The kittens grew bigger and bigger.

One day Pete made his peanut butter sandwich at the kitchen counter. One little black kitten stalked him from behind and made a flying leap.

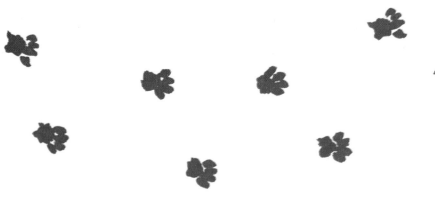

"Peanut butter pawprints? On my kitchen counter?" asked his mother. She frowned as she handed him a cloth.

There was a ripping sound behind them.

"My curtains!" she cried.

Mr. Taylor took the kitten off the curtains. "I think it's time the kittens learned about the big outdoors," he said firmly.

Lady and her kittens were shut in the backyard. All went well for a few days. Then the neighborhood dogs discovered the kittens. The noise was awful! Even Pete put his hands over his ears.

"Sorry, son," Pete's father said. "They've got to go. You know we will find good homes for them."

Pete was not surprised to find the kittens gone when he came home from school the next day. He ran to the back yard. Lady lay in the grass, her head on her paws. She didn't look up.

"Dad," Pete said as he stopped beside his father. "She sure looks lonely."

"Just watch," said Mr. Taylor. There was a slight movement on the doghouse roof. A small black bundle of fur stretched and arched its back lazily. The kitten looked at the gloomy dog below. It switched its tail back and forth. Then it sprang!

"Woof!" barked the surprised dog.

Away dashed the kitten with Lady happily chasing it.

"We left one for Lady," said Mr. Taylor. "I think she will have her paws full!"

Annie Sullivan

(a true story)

Tewksbury

"What is this place? Where are we?" Ten-year-old Annie Sullivan clutched her brother Jimmie's arm. She rubbed her red, puffy eyes, trying to see better. Her eyes were swollen, not because she had been crying, but because of a sickness that had left her almost blind.

"This is Tewksbury," answered the man. "You and your little brother will be living here for a while."

In the late 1800s, Tewksbury was the place where poor people were sometimes sent. Many of the people there were old or sick. Annie and Jimmie were both very sick children with no mother or father to care for them.

While they were at Tewksbury, Jimmie became weaker and weaker. He died only a few months after they arrived. "Now I don't have anyone to love," Annie sighed to herself.

As the days went by, the old women became Annie's only friends. Annie loved to listen to the stories they told her, and she loved to look at the pictures in their books. But it wasn't long before Annie made a wonderful discovery. She found a pretty girl about her age who could read.

Annie listened as her friend read to her. The girl stumbled over long words and sometimes skipped two or three pages at a time.

"When I learn to read, I'm going to read well," Annie thought to herself.

Annie told her wishes to a lady in charge of Tewksbury. "Oh, Miss Maggie," she sighed, "if only I could see better, I'd go to school and learn to read."

Maggie thought for a moment. "I have heard of a school where they teach blind people to read, but—"

"You have? Really?" Annie asked. "They could teach me, couldn't they?"

"Yes, they could teach you. But it costs money to go there. And you don't have any," Maggie said sadly. "You may as well face it, Annie Sullivan. You're going to be here at Tewksbury for the rest of your life."

"Oh, no, I won't," Annie answered. "Somehow, I'm going to go to that school and learn to read!"

Perkins

The thought of school never left Annie's mind. She dreamed of the day she could go there. Then one day some men came to inspect Tewksbury.

"This is your chance, Annie," whispered a friend. "One of those men knows about that school for the blind. I think it's called Perkins. Mention it to Mr. Sanborn."

163

Annie wanted to learn to read so badly that she ran right up to the men just as they were about to leave. "Mr. Sanborn!" she cried. "I want to learn to read! Please let me go to Perkins!"

Annie was sent back to her room without an answer. But she didn't give up. Several weeks went by. Then one day she heard her friend Maggie call to her.

"Annie, Annie! I have wonderful news! This letter says that you can go to Perkins School for the Blind . . . and you won't have to pay anything!"

Annie grabbed Maggie and hugged her. "I'm going to school! I'm going to learn to read!"

The months passed slowly. Finally September came, and Annie went to Perkins. Though she was almost fifteen years old, she felt as excited as a six-year-old about to start the first grade.

And when Annie got to Perkins, the teachers did put her in the first grade.

The first graders at the blind school couldn't see Annie, but they knew she was much older than they were.

"Big Annie! Big Annie!" they teased.

Annie kept her temper. "I'll put up with anything as long as I can learn to read," she said to herself.

Because Annie's eyes were so bad, she learned to read raised letters by feeling their shape. She would sit for hours without even changing positions. She read stories about princes and giants, stories about great leaders of history, and stories about Bible heroes. "It's like a whole new world inside books!" she thought to herself. "My dream has come true!"

Annie also learned to "talk" with a lady at Perkins who was blind and deaf. She spelled words by touching the lady's hand with her fingers.

Not long before Annie finished school something happened that she hadn't even dreamed about for a long time. A doctor

decided to try an operation on her eyes.
When the last strip of cloth was taken off,
the doctor asked, "Annie, can you see me?"

Annie gasped. "I can see you! I can see
the nurse and the bed and the window!
And it's all so beautiful!" She hugged the
doctor. "I'm not blind anymore!"

Tuscumbia

"I have a letter you might like to see," a friend at Perkins said to Annie one day. "A family in Alabama has a six-year-old daughter who can't see or hear. She needs a good teacher. Would you be interested in the job?"

Annie thought about the idea for a moment. A girl who couldn't see or hear! How could she possibly teach a child like that? But it didn't take much discussion to help her decide. "It will be a big job," Annie said. "But I'm willing to try."

Annie didn't have much to pack. In just a few days she was on the train headed for the Keller home in Tuscumbia, Alabama. She stared out the window, thinking about the little girl who couldn't see or hear. The clack-a-clack, clack-a-clack of the wheels rumbled beneath her. "Blind and deaf, blind and deaf," they seemed to say.

"But I was blind too," Annie reminded herself. "And I know the finger alphabet. I'm sure I can help her to understand me. I'll do my best for Helen Keller."

When Annie got to the Kellers' house, the first thing she saw was a little girl with messy hair and a dirty dress. "That must be Helen," she thought. Annie gave Helen the doll she had brought for her.

At supper the little girl sat beside Annie. Annie watched as Helen's mother tried to get her to eat. Helen just threw her food and then ran away from the table.

"It's not strange that she acts the way she does," Annie said. "Helen can't see us and she can't hear our voices. So many things happen around her that she doesn't understand. She needs to learn words."

"That's why we've brought you here to teach her, Miss Sullivan," Helen's father said.

Annie went to find Helen. She picked up
the doll and handed it to Helen. Then she
spelled the word *d-o-l-l* into Helen's hand.

Soon Helen learned how to repeat the hand spellings with her fingers. But Annie could tell that Helen didn't understand that d-o-l-l meant the lovable thing that she held in her arms, or that c-a-k-e meant that food that tasted good. Every session was like a game to Helen.

"How will I ever make her understand?" Annie asked herself a hundred times.

Several months later, Annie and Helen went outside to the water pump for a drink. Helen pushed her arms under the water, and Annie, just the way she always did, spelled the word into Helen's hand. "W-a-t-e-r, w-a-t-e-r," she spelled over and over as the cool liquid gushed over Helen's hands and arms.

Suddenly, Helen stood straight up and eagerly spelled the word back into Annie's hand again and again. Annie realized that something was different.

"She understands! She understands!"
Annie cried. "Oh Helen, you understand
what words are! Now I can teach you to
talk with your fingers just as well as anybody else can talk with his mouth."

Annie began to teach Helen other words.
This time Helen was eager to learn.

Annie Sullivan had freed Helen Keller
from her dark, silent prison!

The Pineyridge Snowstorm

(a Paul Bunyan tall tale)

Snowstorm!

At the first flurry of snow, the lumber-jacks dropped their axes and scrambled up the nearest trees. Snow quickly piled up beneath them as the flurry turned into the first snowstorm of the year. Many, many feet of snow covered the ground in an hour. The lumberjacks climbed higher into the treetops as their camp disappeared under the snow.

Johnny Inkslinger clung to his icy branch.
He wished that he had not stepped outside
the door for a breath of air.

"Brr!" shivered the little bookkeeper. "If
only Paul Bunyan were here," he said to
himself. "He would rescue us!"

Far above him, Johnny saw a big hole.
Shaking with cold, he climbed up. Soon he
was curled up in the hollow tree, fast
asleep.

Johnny didn't know it, but Paul Bunyan
wasn't far away. Paul had been away visiting
his other logging camps. The camps were
strung across the north from Maine to
California. But now he was on his way

back to Pineyridge. He walked along slowly, taking only mile-long steps. Suddenly Paul shivered and pulled up the collar of his wool shirt.

Babe, the famous blue ox, saw the snow first. She tossed her enormous horns and began to trot.

"Whoa, Babe!" called Paul. "People will think there's an earthquake!"

The lumberjacks waved their hats and cheered when they saw Paul.

"I guess it's a good thing that wasn't a big snowstorm," chuckled Paul as he took them out of the trees. "Even the trees would have been covered then!"

As he looked around, Paul saw a wisp of blue smoke coming from a snowdrift. He tunneled down to the cookhouse and wiped off a window. When he peered inside, the busy cooks hardly looked up.

"Weren't you scared?" Paul called to Flapjack Freddy.

"Scared? Of what?" replied the cook.

"Why, scared of the snowstorm," Paul said.

"Too busy!" muttered the chief cook. "Too busy to look outside!"

"Watch out there," Flapjack called as one of the boys almost skated off the edge of the giant griddle. It smoked and hissed as the boys skated around with big slabs of bacon strapped to their feet.

"Ready with the batter!" Flapjack waved to the other cooks. They rolled the huge barrel of pancake batter over to the griddle. Other cooks stood ready with snow shovels to turn the pancakes as the batter was piped onto the hot griddle.

"I know why you didn't see the snow." Paul laughed. "You were too busy! Now I had better get busy myself."

The Hollow Tree

"Get some snowshoes and some more axes, men," Paul said. "We have ten thousand trees to deliver!"

Paul harnessed Babe and dug out some big logging chains. He looped one end of the chain around a treetop and the other to Babe's harness.

"Pull, Babe," the men shouted. Babe tossed her horns and pulled. Pop! The tree flew out of the snow like a rabbit out of his hole!

The men went to work chopping off the tree branches. Paul and Babe moved on to another treetop. Soon ten thousand logs were piled on the hill beside Pineyridge River.

"The ice is too thick," said Paul's foreman, Whistling Willie. "The logs won't break it. How will we get them downriver?"

Paul grinned and called for Babe. She pawed the snow as he unhitched the chains. Then with a huge leap, the blue ox slid down the hill. Babe hit the ice so hard that it broke into tiny pieces and fell as hail all the way to Boston!

Paul gave the logs a push and they rolled into the water with a mighty splash. Down the river they floated. "Hooray!" the men shouted as the dinner bell rang.

"Time to eat," cried Paul.

The men laughed and talked as they sat down at the long tables. The cooks strapped

on their roller skates and picked up the huge platters full of food. Up and down the long room they skated.

"That's strange," Flapjack Freddy said, tapping Paul on the elbow. "I can't find Johnny."

Paul looked down the table. There was only an empty chair where the bookkeeper usually sat.

"Where is Johnny?" Paul asked.

"He was in a tree the last time I saw him," answered Bart.

"He curled up in a hole to keep warm," said another lumberjack.

"A hole? In a tree?"

The men looked at Paul. Paul looked at them. Johnny was in one of the trees floating down the river! He would go over the waterfall!

Paul and his men ran to the riverbank. "We'll never catch up to those logs," cried one of the men.

"Come here, Babe," called Paul. He whispered in her ear. Babe leaned over the river and began to drink. She drank and drank and drank. At last the river was empty. Only the muddy bottom of the riverbed was left. Far down the riverbed they could see the piled up logs. Paul began to run. The mud pulled at his boots at every step he took. When he reached the logs, the men lost sight of him. At last he returned, but where was Johnny!

The men sank down on the riverbank and put their heads in their hands. Paul reached into his pocket. He brought out Johnny, still curled up and still asleep!

A happy roar burst from the men. Johnny blinked and sat up. "What happened?" he asked as he looked around. "Where is the river?"

"Wait and see," replied Paul cheerfully. He twisted the pipe of the cookhouse stove. Then he blew and blew until the stove glowed red hot. It melted the snow all around the river.

The snow ran down the banks and filled up the riverbed. Again down the river floated ten thousand logs—no, it was nine thousand, nine hundred, ninety-nine. Paul couldn't charge the sawmill owner for the hollow log. After all, it could never be said that Paul Bunyan cheated!

Little Things

Little drops of water,
Little grains of sand,
Make the mighty ocean
And the pleasant land.

Little deeds of kindness,
Little words of love,
Please all those around us
And please our God above.

by Julia A. F. Carney—Adapted

MAKING MELODY

O, Say, Can You See?

(based on historical research)

Francis Scott Key walked back and forth along the deck of the ship.

"Can we go faster?" he asked as he stopped beside the captain and Colonel Skinner. "We must catch up to the British fleet."

"We're going as fast as we can, sir," answered the captain. "Dr. Beanes is a friend of yours, isn't he?"

Lieutenant Key nodded. "Yes, he is. When I heard that Dr. Beanes had been arrested by the British, I went to see the President. He said that Colonel Skinner and I could try to get the doctor released."

"Yes," said the colonel. "I brought some letters from British soldiers. They tell how Dr. Beanes helped them. The doctor was kind enough to treat the wounded on both sides of a battle."

186

"Look!" The captain pointed ahead. "There is the British fleet now."

Lieutenant Key leaned on the rail. "They are coming back this way!" he said. "I'm glad we're flying the truce flag!"

The other two men came to stand beside him.

"There are over forty ships," said the captain. "The British admiral has joined another fleet of ships."

"So that is why they are coming back." The colonel frowned. "Now he has enough ships to attack Fort McHenry!"

The men watched the long line of ships come closer.

"There is the flagship." The captain pointed to one of the larger battleships.

"Hello," called the colonel to the men on board the flagship. "May we come aboard?"

Soon the answer came back. "Yes."

Colonel Skinner and Lieutenant Key climbed down into a rowboat. They rowed to the flagship and were helped aboard. Hours passed.

From time to time the captain left his cabin to look up at the huge battleship. At last he heard voices, then the rattle of oars. The rowboat thumped against the side of the ship. The captain helped three men back on board. "You must be Dr. Beanes," he said, shaking the third man's hand.

"Yes," Dr. Beanes said, smiling. "The letters helped the admiral decide to release me." Then his smile disappeared. "But we are all prisoners until the battle with Fort McHenry is over."

"I was afraid of that," said the captain. "If they let us go now, we could tell the people at the fort about the attack."

The sky was dark as the little ship sailed with the British ships into the harbor.

Silently the men watched the busy sailors prepare for battle.

At last the harbor was quiet and still. The dark line of ships waited.

"Fire!" came the command from the flagship. A cannon roared. Then the other ships began firing across the harbor.

The men stared into the darkness. Then as a rocket exploded above the fort, they saw the Stars and Stripes flying.

"The flag is still there!" Dr. Beanes shouted. "The fort has not fallen yet!"

All night Lieutenant Key paced the deck of the little ship. From time to time he could see the flag. Then, just before dawn, the noise stopped.

"Is the flag still there?" The men peered into the darkness, but they could see nothing. Not a sound disturbed the strange quiet. At last the sky began to glow with the early morning light. Patches of fog and smoke lifted for a moment. The men could barely see the flagpole above the fort.

"The flag?" asked Lieutenant Key.

Something fluttered on the flagpole. Then the torn flag could be seen waving in the morning breeze.

"The flag is still there!" Lieutenant Key cried as the captain and his crew cheered. "The flag is still there!"

Reaching for a piece of paper, Francis Scott Key began to write:

O, say, can you see by the dawn's early
light,
What so proudly we hailed at the
twilight's last gleaming?
Whose broad stripes and bright stars,
through the perilous fight,
O'er the ramparts we watched, were
so gallantly streaming?
And the rocket's red glare, the bombs
bursting in air,
Gave proof through the night that our
flag was still there.
O, say, does that star-spangled banner
yet wave
O'er the land of the free, and the
home of the brave?

The Nightingale

(adapted from a story by
Hans Christian Andersen)

A Plain Little Bird

Long ago in China there lived a mighty emperor who loved beautiful things. His gardens were full of the loveliest of flowers in China. Little silver bells hung beside the flowers. The bells rang gently when people walked by the flowers.

The Emperor's gardens stretched on and on until they led to a huge forest. At the edge of this forest there lived a nightingale.

The nightingale sang every night. He sang so sweetly that everyone who heard him would stop to listen.

People came from all over the world to admire the Emperor's palace and gardens. But when they heard the nightingale, they all decided that it was better than anything else they had seen or heard. Great people wrote stories and poems and even books about the lovely nightingale of China.

One day the Emperor of China received a book from the Emperor of Japan. It had been written about China. The Emperor enjoyed all the parts that told about his palace and his gardens. "But the nightingale is the best," said the book.

The Emperor called his most trusted servant. "Where is this nightingale?" he demanded. "Why haven't I heard about him? The things the book says about his song sound too wonderful to believe."

The servant looked surprised. "I'm sorry,

your Majesty, but I haven't heard of the nightingale either," he answered.

"I want him presented to me at once!" the Emperor ordered.

The servant bowed and hurried out of the room. All through the palace he ran, asking every lord and lady he met about the bird. But none of them had heard of the nightingale. He ran back to the Emperor and said, "Your Majesty, the nightingale must be a story that these writers made up."

"If that nightingale isn't here tonight, everyone will be sent to bed without supper!" shouted the Emperor.

This time all the court searched for someone who knew about the nightingale, because they didn't like the idea of going to bed without supper. At last one little kitchen maid was found who had heard the bird.

"Oh, yes, the nightingale can sing gloriously," she said. "I pass him at the edge of the forest when I go home each night. Sometimes he even comes when I call him and lights on my finger."

"Little kitchen maid," said the servant, "please find that nightingale for us."

So the kitchen maid led the way, and the people of the court followed. On the way they heard a cow mooing.

"Oh, that's the nightingale!" they shouted. "What a strong voice it has."

"No, no," said the kitchen maid. "That's just a cow. We're still far away from the nightingale."

As they walked farther, they heard a frog croaking. "How beautiful!" exclaimed the court musician. "Is that the nightingale?"

"No, that's just a frog," the kitchen maid replied. "But we may hear the nightingale soon."

As the girl spoke, the nightingale began to sing. "There he is!" She pointed to the little brown bird.

"Oh, my!" exclaimed all the court. "To think that such a tiny, plain-looking bird could sing such a lovely song!" For a while they just stood and listened.

"Little girl, call the nightingale down to light on your finger," commanded the chief servant. "We must take him to the Emperor."

The nightingale lighted on the kitchen maid's finger and sang all the way back to the palace. "Oh, what a lovely song," sighed all the court attendants.

At the palace the nightingale sang so sweetly that tears came to the Emperor's eyes. "We will give the nightingale his own cage," the Emperor declared.

So from that night on the nightingale lived at the palace. He could go outside twice a day, but twelve servants went with him, each holding a ribbon tied to the bird's legs. The poor nightingale didn't enjoy this at all.

One day the Emperor received a box labeled "The Nightingale."

"Oh, it must be another book about our famous bird," said the Emperor, and he opened it with delight. But inside he did not see a book.

Inside the box there was a bird. But it wasn't a real bird. It was made of gold and silver, with jewels of all kinds on its wings and tail. A ribbon hung on its neck that said, "The Emperor of Japan's nightingale is better than the Emperor of China's nightingale."

The Best Song

When the golden nightingale was wound up, it sang a lovely song that was much like the song the real nightingale sang. While it sang, its tail moved up and down, glistening with silver and gold.

"How pretty!" all the court exclaimed. "The two birds must sing together."

But that didn't work at all, for the real nightingale sang in one way and the golden nightingale sang in another way. So the Emperor decided they would listen to the golden bird sing alone again.

Everyone thought the song was just as lovely as the real nightingale's. And they all agreed that the new bird was much prettier to look at than the plain brown bird.

The golden nightingale sang the same song thirty-three times and it didn't get tired. The people wanted to hear it again, but the Emperor stopped them.

"We'll hear the real nightingale sing now," he said.

But no one could find the real nightingale. He had flown out the window and back to the forest he loved.

"What an ungrateful bird!" exclaimed all the court in anger. "But we still have the best one."

And the golden nightingale was wound to sing the same song once more.

The court musician praised the bird. "You can never tell what the real nightingale is going to sing, but we know ahead of time what this bird will do. We can even open it up and show others how it works. Your Majesty, this bird is far better than the real nightingale."

"Just what we thought!" the whole court agreed.

The real nightingale was banished from the empire, and the golden one was given a place of great respect. Long books were written about it, telling how wonderful it was.

And so a whole year passed. Everyone in the kingdom learned the golden nightingale's song, and this was the very reason they loved it so much.

But one evening when the Emperor lay in bed listening to the golden nightingale's song, he heard something unusual. "Whirr, clack, clack," the bird said.

The Emperor sat up to look. The bird was twisting and then it stopped with a "twang"!

"It's broken!" he cried. He called the court watchmaker. The watchmaker fixed the bird, but he said that it must be treated very carefully because its gears were wearing out. The Emperor declared that the golden nightingale could be played only once a year.

And so five whole years went by. But then a sad thing happened. The Emperor got very sick. All the people of the court were sure he was about to die.

The Emperor lay in his great golden bed. He tossed and turned, shaking from his fever.

"Little golden nightingale, sing for me," he cried. "Please sing to drive my fever away!" But the golden nightingale didn't move.

The night was fearfully quiet.

Suddenly through the silence, a lovely song filled the room. It was the real nightingale, perched on a branch outside the Emperor's window!

"Oh, little nightingale, you came back to me." The Emperor sighed with relief. He lay very still, listening to the nightingale's song. The lovely song brought sweet thoughts to his mind. He thought of the garden where the roses bloomed and the silver bells tinkled. He thought of the cool green forest where the breezes blew. As he lay quietly thinking of these pleasant things, he began to feel better.

"Little nightingale, I banished you from my kingdom and you still came back to help me get well. How can I ever thank you?"

The little brown bird flicked his tail and sang even more sweetly.

"I understand," said the Emperor. "You don't want to be kept in a cage. Little nightingale, you may be free to fly around your green forest. But please sing at my window every night."

The nightingale bobbed his little head as if he understood. Then he sang a song that helped the Emperor sleep. Oh, what a sweet, refreshing sleep that was!

The next morning the servants came in, expecting to find their Emperor still very sick. Instead he stood up and greeted them with a smile. "The nightingale—the *real* nightingale—sang a song that helped me get well. His music is the best an emperor could ever want."

Song of Faith

(based on II Chronicles 20:1-30)

A Worried King

"Armies? Armies coming to fight us?" The whispers spread through all the country of Judah. "Armies have not tried to fight us for years! Why would they come now?"

Worried people came out of their houses to talk with each other. "Let's go to Jerusalem," some suggested. "We need to help the king." Everywhere people could be seen getting ready to leave for the capital city.

The fathers said, "Bring enough water for the trip. The road is long and the sun is hot."

The mothers said, "Come, come, children. Leave your toys and games. Hold on to our hands. We do not want you getting lost in the crowd."

Servants and masters, men and women, old people, young people, and little children all left their houses and headed for Jerusalem. The road overflowed with travelers.

In Jerusalem King Jehoshaphat sat in the palace, thinking and praying. He knew that the people of Judah were worried about the invading armies. He bowed his head in prayer. "Lord, please show me what to do."

A messenger entered the room and knelt before the king. "Your Majesty, all the people of Judah are gathered together. They are standing outside waiting for you to speak."

"That is good," answered the king. "I want to talk to the Lord where all the

people can hear me. They need to pray too."

The messenger left. King Jehoshaphat went to the temple to stand before all the people.

As soon as the people saw him, they became quiet. Men stopped arguing about the armies. Women stopped talking with each other. Boys and girls stopped playing. Even the little babies were hushed. Everyone wanted to hear what the king would say.

Jehoshaphat cleared his throat and spoke. But he did not speak to the people. He spoke to God. "Oh, Lord," he began, "You are the God that we serve. No one is as strong and powerful as You. You helped us to drive our enemies out of this land. And now, Lord, the wicked people of Moab and Ammon are coming to fight against us. Please judge them, because we are powerless against them. We do not know what to do, but we look to You for help."

210

All the people silently prayed with Jehoshaphat. When his prayer ended, they remained silent, praying in their hearts.

The stillness was broken by the voice of one man. "Listen to me, O King, and all you people of Judah. The Lord has given me the answer." The man pressed through the crowd to reach the king. People whispered to each other, "Who is he?"

"I think he is Jahaziel," others answered. "He is a godly man. God must have spoken to him. He has something to tell us."

When Jahaziel came to the front, everyone became quiet again. "People of Judah," he began, "we will not have to fight as we usually do. The Lord is with us. He will fight for us. All we have to do is watch!"

The Singing Army

Jehoshaphat listened closely to what Jahaziel said. "Do you mean that we will not have to fight at all?" he asked.

"That is right," answered Jahaziel. "God has told me that tomorrow morning everyone should go down to the valley. That is where the enemy will be. You do not need to take any armor with you. The Lord will do all the fighting."

Jehoshaphat and all the people of Judah could hardly believe this exciting news when they heard it. At first the people murmured. But then they saw Jehoshaphat kneel to worship the Lord. Then they knelt too, worshiping the Lord.

Then Jahaziel and some other people stood up and began to sing. As loudly as they could, they all sang choruses of praise and glory to God. "Give thanks to the Lord, for His mercy is great," they sang.

"Worship him for His loving-kindness." All the people listened to the beautiful music. God listened too, and He was pleased.

"That is what we will do!" cried the king. "Tomorrow morning we will go to the valley to wait for the Lord to fight our battle for us. We will have no spears or shields. We will have no bows and arrows. But we will not stand quietly. We will sing, giving God the glory for the great victory He will give us."

The people cheered. Everyone was excited about the great victory they would have the next day.

Early in the morning all the people of Judah gathered together in the valley just as King Jehoshaphat had told them. They didn't talk loudly, but excitement was in the air.

King Jehoshaphat stood to get their attention. "Listen, people of Judah. Believe the Lord your God. Believe His prophets, and our nation will always be strong."

Then the king chose the ones that he knew were the very best singers. "You lead the people, singing praises to the Lord," he instructed.

And so they marched, without swords, spears, or shields. The singers sang their song beautifully. "Praise the Lord, for His mercy endureth forever," and their song echoed against the great hills surrounding the valley.

A messenger came running up. "King Jehoshaphat!" he cried. "I saw the enemy armies. It looked as if they were fighting each other!"

The king smiled and the singers sang their song more loudly than ever. "Praise the Lord, for His mercy endureth forever."

At last the people came to the watch-tower in the wilderness. Some men climbed up to see what they could see. The whole valley was quiet. Not a sound could be heard.

"All the enemy armies have killed each other!" the men shouted.

"God is faithful!" cried King Jehoshaphat. "We didn't have to fight at all. God has given us the victory!"

What joyful singing there was when the people returned to Jerusalem! "Praise the Lord, for His mercy endureth forever," they all sang.

And God listened to them. And He was pleased.

Melody Breeze

The round, golden sun smiled down on the earth, warming it with his gentle rays. But he was interrupted by a whooshing sound around him. "One of the little breezes has come to visit," he thought.

The breeze that came was one of the newest ones, Melody Breeze. She whirled and twirled all around Mr. Sun.

"Slow down, little one," Mr. Sun chuckled. "Are you having trouble doing your job? Is there something about your work that you need to know?"

"Yes," answered Melody, whirling and twirling even harder. "I want to know just what my job is. I've asked all the other breezes, and I don't especially like what they tell me."

Mr. Sun smiled. "There's nothing hard about your job," he said. "Your job is to make music. To do that, you must gently blow close to the earth."

"I thought so." Melody Breeze sniffed in disgust. "Your answer is just like the ones I got from everybody else. Blow close to the earth!"

"Have you even tried it yet?" Mr. Sun asked.

"No. I haven't tried it," Melody huffed. "I don't plan to try it. I can make much more beautiful music blowing high up in the sky. I've seen Meadowlark. He comes flying high up into the sky before he even starts to sing. That's a much grander thing to do than singing near the earth. And he's only a bird!" She sniffed again. "I'll show you that I can do my job best where I choose to do it." And she blew away as hard as she could.

"Whee!" Melody blew here and there through all the wide sky while old Mr. Sun watched. "Whoosh," she puffed. "I can make music up in the sky!"

Melody Breeze blew so hard and so loudly that she whipped right past Meadowlark without even seeing him. Poor Meadowlark had been singing his best, but when she came whooshing by, two feathers fluttered away.

"Where did that wind come from?" he gasped. Meadowlark caught his breath and chased after Melody Breeze. "What are you doing up here?" he demanded.

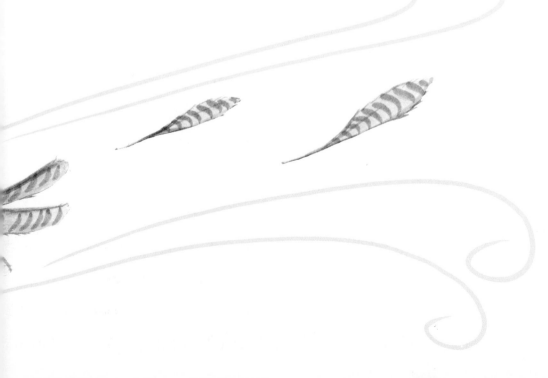

"I'm making music!" Melody blew far away.

"Music? I don't hear any music," Meadowlark said. "I'm going to see Mr. Sun about this."

When Meadowlark arrived, he found that several other birds were there before him. All of them had the same complaint— Melody Breeze.

"She ruffled my feathers!" cried one. "And she wasn't even sorry!"

"She blew my song away before I could even start singing it!" cried another.

Meadowlark interrupted. "She says she's making music, but I don't hear any!" he exclaimed.

Mr. Sun sighed. "Melody Breeze will soon change," he promised. "Just wait and see."

So all the birds flew back to their nests to wait until Melody Breeze became quiet.

It wasn't long before the little breeze saw that she was the only one in the sky. She slowed down.

Then she realized that she couldn't hear any music.

"Everybody's gone," she murmured to herself, "and I'm not making any music."

It was a quiet little breeze that puffed her way back to Mr. Sun. "I'm lonely up there in the sky," she admitted. "And I would especially like to make real music."

"Poor little one," said Mr. Sun. "Would you like to try blowing gently near the earth now?"

Melody nodded. Gently she drifted down to the trees. Her quiet little puffs softly rustled the leaves.

"Listen to the music up in the trees!" The birds and animals stopped what they were doing to hear the gentle rustling.

The squirrel family had hung empty acorn shells on strings outside their front door, and Melody rattled them lightly.

"What a fun sound!" the little squirrels exclaimed. "That's a kind of music too!"

Melody whistled gently through the cracks in old Mr. Rabbit's house. "Why, this is much better than what I was doing before," she said, and she rustled the long grass in the field.

"Is that really Melody Breeze that we're hearing?" The birds could hardly believe it. They flew high up into the sky to celebrate in song.

At last Melody Breeze was doing her job.

Obedience

(a true story)

On the way home from a revival meeting, five-year-old Becky said, "Daddy, I learned three things in my class tonight."

"What did you learn, Becky?" Mr. Greene asked.

"I learned that I'm supposed to do everything you and Mother tell me to do," Becky replied.

"That's good!" Mr. Greene said.

Mrs. Greene turned to smile at Becky.

"But that's not all, Daddy." Becky leaned closer. "I'm supposed to do it when you say to do it."

"Really?" Mr. Greene asked.

"And, Daddy, there's one more thing." Becky could hardly wait to tell the rest. "I'm supposed to do what you and Mother say with a 'happy' on my face!"

Everyone laughed.

"That's cute," said Becky's sister.

"And it's also true," said Mr. Greene. "You really listened well in your class, Becky."

"Yes," said Mrs. Greene. "We all need to remember what Becky learned tonight."

After that, when one of the six Greene children was tempted to disobey, he was reminded of Becky's lesson:

to do what I'm told,

to do it when I'm told,

and to do it with a 'happy' on my face.

227

One day in the spring, the Greenes were traveling to North Carolina. When the children got restless from the long drive, Mrs. Greene began singing songs. They sang all the songs they liked best.

"What will we sing next, Mother?" they asked.

"Why don't we make up our own song?" she suggested. "We could make up the tune too."

"What could we sing about?" Susan asked.

"You know," said Mr. Greene as he stopped at a traffic light, "people remember ideas when they are put to music. Why don't we take the three ideas from Becky's lesson and put them to music?"

"That would be fun," said Becky.

"Yes, Becky's lesson would make a good song about obedience," said Mother.

"There's a verse in I John that says something about knowing what we believe by our obedience to God," Mr. Greene replied.

The girls found a Bible and began looking through I John for the verse Mr. Greene was thinking about.

"Here it is!" Susan said.

Susan read from the Bible. "I John 2:3. 'And hereby we do know that we know Him, if we keep His commandments. '"

"Keeping His commandments is obedience," said Rick. "Why don't we spell *obedience* as part of the song?"

"How's this?" Mr. Greene sang, "O-B-E-D-I-E-N-C-E."

And Mrs. Green finished, "Obedience is the very best way to show that you believe."

"We like it!" cried the children.

"Where is the tape recorder?" asked Mr. Greene. "Let's tape it before we forget it."

The children found the tape recorder and put it on the seat between Mr. and Mrs. Greene. Together they recorded the song.

"Could we write another part to the song that says what obedience means?" asked Susan.

"How about a verse that explains the three principles in Becky's lesson?" Mrs. Greene suggested.

The family tried different words, singing them to a tune. They kept changing the tune to fit the words. Finally the beginning of a new song was recorded on the tape.

The children sang the new song over and over. When the family returned home, they sang the song for their friends. It was not long before a new verse was added to the song.

Sometime later, Mrs. Greene was asked to be a judge in a music contest at a Christian school. She and another judge began to discuss the need for new children's songs that would teach godly principles. Mrs. Greene sang the "Obedience" song for him. The judge asked her to write out the words and music so it could be published for boys and girls to learn and sing.

Today children and adults all over the world sing "Obedience." God used the words of a teacher in a class for five-year-old children to give us a song that reminds people to be obedient to Him.

Obedience

Mike & Ruth Greene

Mike & Ruth Greene

1. O - bed - i - ence is the ver - y best way to show that you be - lieve.
2. We want to live pure, we want to live clean, we want to do our best;

Do - ing ex - act - ly what the Lord com - mands, Do - ing it hap - pi - ly.
Sweet - ly sub - mit - ting to au - thor - i - ty, Leav - ing to God the rest.

Ac - tion is the key, Do it im - med - i - ate - ly. Joy you will re - ceive. O -
Walk - ing in the light, keep - ing our at - ti - tude right, On the nar - row way; For

bed - i - ence is the ver - y best way to show that you be - lieve.
if we be - lieve the Word we re - ceive, we al - ways will o - bey.

Chorus

O - B - E - D - I - E - N - C - E, O -

bed - i - ence is the ver - y best way to show that you be - lieve.

232

Granny Nell's Dulcimer

The Dulcimer

For just a moment Tansy looked down at
the crystal clear water and almost lost her
balance. Her thin arms waved in the air as
she tried to keep from falling. Then, putting
one foot in front of the other, she edged
carefully across the log.

"Whew! I thought I was going to fall in!" She let out her breath and sat down on a stump.

A blue jay chattered at her from a nearby tree. He seemed to be making fun of her.

"Oh, hush," Tansy frowned. "I know it's a small stream, but who wants to get wet!"

The bird hopped back and forth across the twig, scolding Tansy. Then he stopped, tilting his head to one side to listen. Faint music drifted down the trail.

"What's that?" Tansy whispered. She stood up and brushed off her skirt. As Tansy crept up the trail, the music became louder. She pushed the leaves aside and stared at an old gray cabin. Tansy left her hiding place and moved quietly around the stone chimney. An old woman sat on the porch, holding an instrument in her lap. As Tansy watched, the woman plucked the strings with something that looked like a feather.

Tansy closed her eyes and listened. The music made her think of sunshine and laughter and faraway places.

"Come here, child."

Tansy jumped and opened her eyes.

"Well, come on up here where I can get a look at you." The woman motioned her closer.

Tansy slowly climbed the steps and stood in front of the rocker.

"You must have come up the back way," said the woman. "Not many people use that trail nowadays. Do you live around here?"

"Yes, ma'am, we just moved back here," Tansy said.

"Folks around here call me Granny," the old woman said. The rocker creaked as she leaned back. "You must be Jim and Nora Ledford's daughter."

Tansy's eyes widened. "How did you know?"

"I just guessed," said the woman. "You look like your mother did when she was about your age. I know your folks from way back. Ask your mother about old Granny Nell." She patted the rocker next to her. "Come and sit down."

Tansy pulled the rocker closer to Granny Nell and sat down. Granny slid a dried chicken bone up and down the strings of her instrument. With her right hand she plucked the strings with a turkey quill.

As Granny played one song after another, Tansy discovered that she knew some of the tunes.

"Just watch," Granny whispered. She began to play a lively tune called "Turkey in the Straw." A tiny head popped out of the branches next to the porch. Then a squirrel scampered out on a limb. Tansy clapped her hands over her mouth to keep from laughing as he hopped up and down. It looked just like he was keeping time to the music.

"Sh," warned Granny Nell. Tansy sat very still. Granny played "Pop Goes the Weasel." A flock of blue jays swooped down into the yard. They flew around the yard, diving at each other.

Tansy's eyes were bright with laughter when Granny Nell finally stopped playing. "Do they always come up when you play?" Tansy asked.

"I usually play the same time every day," Granny replied. "My little friends wouldn't know what to do without their afternoon music." She ran her fingers over the strings.

"What is that thing you're playing?" Tansy asked.

"A dulcimer," Granny replied. "An old-time dulcimer that belonged to my mother." She looked at the sun. "You had better be on your way before the sun sets. Come back tomorrow and I'll show you how to play the dulcimer."

"Will you, for sure?" Tansy asked.

"Sure will," Granny replied. "Now scoot!"

Summer on Shady Mountain

All summer long Tansy climbed the back trail to Granny Nell's cabin. The noisy blue jay grew used to her visits. He no longer scolded Tansy when she ran across the log. Instead he greeted her like an old friend.

Today Tansy whistled back at him happily. "Morning, Blue," she called as she hurried past his tree.

At the cabin Tansy found Granny in the kitchen making tea.

"Take the dulcimer outside, Tansy. I'll be right out," she said.

"Play 'Church in the Wildwood,' Tansy," Granny said, sitting down in the other rocker. She tapped her foot in time to the music. Granny nodded to herself as the notes faded. "I've never had anyone learn to play the dulcimer as fast as you have. The good Lord has given you a gift, Tansy. Make sure you use it well."

"But the animals don't come when I play," said Tansy.

"Give them time," Granny said, smiling. "They'll come around soon enough."

"Mother says that you play at the Shady Mountain Fair," Tansy said. "She says you always win the music competition."

Granny nodded. "So far I have. The extra money helps me to pay the taxes on my land."

She looked around her at the honeysuckle vines, heavy with sweet-smelling blossoms. Then she looked out across the valley to the blue-misted mountains.

"I hope I never have to leave my mountains," she said. Then she shook her head as if to clear it of gloomy thoughts. "Let's go for a walk before you go home," she said.

Tansy took many more walks with Granny Nell. Each day Granny showed her something new about life on the mountain. One day it was a pale, speckled egg from a blue jay's nest. The next day it was a tiny wild flower almost hidden under the damp leaves.

One afternoon Tansy skipped up the trail and stopped by the log to watch the rushing water. Whistling for Blue as usual, she started across the log. On the other side she stopped and looked about her. There had been no cheerful answering whistle. Puzzled, she whistled again. There was a sudden flash of blue, and the little blue jay dashed about her head, scolding loudly.

"What's wrong with you?" Tansy asked, ducking her head. Blue just flew up the trail, still scolding.

"All right, I'm coming!" Tansy ran to keep up with him. "Granny Nell!" she called as she ran around the cabin.

Granny Nell was sitting in her rocker. She looked up, her face white with pain.

"What's wrong?" Tansy stopped to catch her breath.

"I slipped on the way to the spring," said Granny. "My arm hit a rock when I fell. I think it's broken."

"I'll get Mother," said Tansy. "We'll bring the car back."

Mrs. Ledford was in the kitchen. She saw Tansy running toward the house and went to meet her.

"What's wrong?" she asked.

"Granny's hurt!" Tansy called. "We need to take her to the doctor!"

Mrs. Ledford wiped her hands and went to get the car. They drove carefully over the bumpy, winding road to Granny's cabin. It took over an hour to get Granny to the clinic. Tansy and her mother waited until the doctor finished with Granny's cast.

"Now you'll stay with us for a few weeks," Mrs. Ledford said.

"Oh, no," said Granny. "I don't want to be a bother—"

"You won't be, Granny." Mrs. Ledford smiled. "You'll always be welcome in our home."

"Please, Granny," Tansy pleaded.

"All right," said Granny, slowly. "If you're sure I'll not be in the way."

"You won't be!" both Tansy and her mother answered.

Mountain Melodies

The next morning Tansy balanced a tray as she knocked on Granny's bedroom door.

"Come in!"

Tansy pushed open the door.

"Let me help," said Granny, starting to get up.

"Wait, Granny," Tansy said. She walked carefully across the room. "There, I made it!" she said. She set the tray down, being careful not to hit Granny's cast.

"Thank you, Tansy," said Granny. She handed Tansy a piece of buttered toast. "Now you can help me eat all this."

Tansy grinned. "Mother did give you a lot, didn't she?" She reached for a slice of bacon. Her hand stopped in midair.

"Granny," she said. "You can't play in the contest with a broken arm!"

"No," Granny replied. "I can't play with one hand. But we do need the dulcimer.

Ask your mother if you can go get it this morning."

Tansy frowned, still thinking about the contest. "But you need the money."

"Now, child," Granny said, "you get that worried look off your face. The Lord has always provided for me. Things have a way of working out when you trust Him."

"All right, Granny," Tansy said. "I'll go ask Mother if I can go now."

"I heard," Mother said as she knocked at the door. "You run along. I need to talk to Granny about something."

Tansy half ran, half walked up the trail. At the log she stopped and whistled for Blue.

Wings flashed in the sunlight as Blue landed on her finger.

"You've never come this close before," Tansy whispered. "You're worried, too, aren't you?" Blue chirped and flew back up the trail.

Tansy followed slowly. At the cabin, she took the dulcimer off the peg. As she started out the door, a tiny animal scampered out onto a limb.

"You miss your music, don't you? Granny Nell didn't get to play for you yesterday."

Tansy sat on the porch steps and began to play the songs Granny had taught her. The squirrel hopped closer, tilting his head to one side.

"So you finally like the way I play," said Tansy. It was then that the thought came to her. "I wonder if I could enter the contest," she said to the little squirrel. "If I win, I could give Granny the money for her taxes."

She held the dulcimer close and walked down the trail to her house.

"Mom, Granny," Tansy called. She stopped at the door of the spare room.

The two women looked up.

"I want to enter the music contest at the fair," Tansy said. "That is, if Granny will let me use her dulcimer."

"Honey, you can't—" Mother stopped as she saw a twinkle in Granny's eyes. Then Mother nodded and began to smile.

"You may use the dulcimer, Tansy. But you need to play a lot," Granny said.

"I will, every day!" said Tansy.

And so she did.

The Contest

Every day Tansy played and sang the old songs. Granny tapped her foot and sang along with her. The day of the contest came closer and closer.

At last Tansy found herself seated on the stage with the other contestants. She clutched the dulcimer tightly in her lap. One of the fiddlers leaned over and patted her on the arm.

"Relax," he said. "Just think of something that you really like and you'll do fine."

250

Tansy looked out across the crowd. Then the announcer's voice could be heard above the noise of the tuning instruments. "And now, our first contestant is Harley Stevens, playing the fiddle."

Soon even Tansy was tapping her foot to the lively music. Each player seemed better than the last. Then came the dreaded announcement: "Our last contestant, Tansy Ledford, is new to the dulcimer, but was taught by the best, Granny Nell!"

Tansy rubbed her hands on her dress and walked to the front of the stage. She sat in the chair the announcer held for her and began to play. At first the beating of her heart seemed louder than the music. Tansy closed her eyes so she wouldn't have to see the people.

Then as she played she thought of Blue's wings flashing in the summer sun. She thought of the smell of honeysuckle, of the light lavender scent in Granny's clothes, and of the smell of Mother's home-baked bread.

253

As the last notes of "Amazing Grace" faded, Tansy opened her eyes. The crowd was quiet. Then as Tansy returned to her seat, they began to clap. The announcer stood up. "All the contestants did a fine job . . . ," he began. Tansy held her breath as he finished his little speech, "and the winner is Harley Stevens!"

Tansy let out her breath slowly. She hadn't won. Slowly she picked up the dulcimer and left the stage. Mother and Granny Nell met her at the steps.

Mother hugged her close. "You played beautifully, Tansy!" she said.

Harley Stevens stopped beside them. "You did a terrific job for such a young one." He turned to Granny. "It won't be long before she plays as well as you do, Granny Nell."

"I think so myself," Granny said proudly.

"But Granny," said Tansy. "I didn't win any money."

Granny put her good arm around Tansy. "Now don't you worry about that. Your mother wants you to have more lessons on the dulcimer. And she wants to pay me to be your teacher." She squeezed Tansy. "There's nothing I would like better!"

Tansy squeezed back happily. "Me either, Granny!"

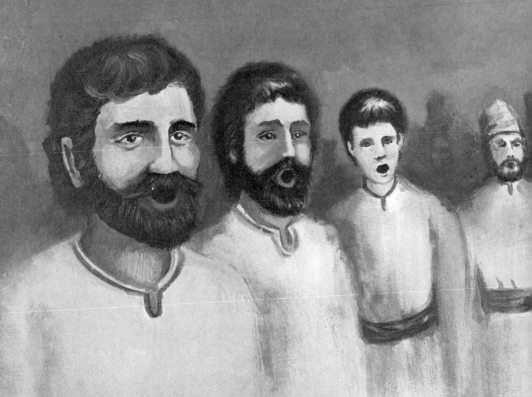

Psalm 33:1-3

Rejoice in the Lord, O ye righteous:

For praise is comely for the upright.

Praise the Lord with harp:

Sing unto him with the psaltery

And an instrument of ten strings.

Sing unto him a new song;

Play skilfully with a loud noise.

257

Fanny Crosby

First Years

Fanny Crosby's mother bundled her up in a thick quilt. She rocked her back and forth until Fanny's sore red eyes closed in sleep. Before long, the whinny of a horse came from the yard, and the doctor knocked at the door. Quickly, Mrs. Crosby led him to Fanny's cradle.

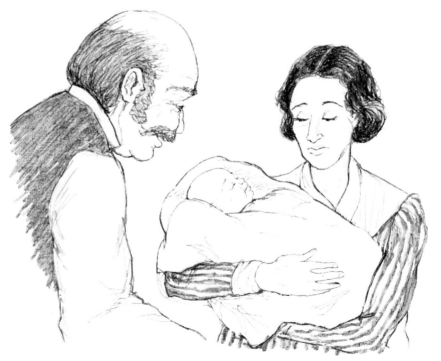

"How old is your little girl?" he asked, as he listened to Fanny's heartbeat.

"Just six weeks old," Mrs. Crosby answered. "Will she be all right? She's had a bit of a cold, but now I'm worried about her eyes. They are red and swollen."

"I'll give you some medicine for her eyes," the doctor said. "She should be well shortly."

Mr. and Mrs. Crosby followed the doctor's directions closely, but Fanny's eyes did not heal. The medicine only made them worse. At last they knew that Fanny could no longer see.

As she grew up, Fanny's blindness did not stop her from climbing trees, riding horseback, and romping through the fields by her home. With her fingers she could "see" everything—especially the face of her dear grandmother.

Grandmother taught Fanny about the beautiful world God had created. Fanny learned the names of the songbirds from Grandmother. When the birds perched on the trees to sing, Fanny listened and listened until she knew their songs by heart.

Grandmother read the Bible to Fanny almost every day. Before long Fanny had memorized whole books of the Bible.

"Fanny!" Mother called early one morning. "We're going to New York. Doctor Mott wants to look at your eyes. Maybe he will be able to help you see."

Even though she could not see, Fanny dressed herself. She put on her best dress and combed her hair.

Before long they were on their way. Fanny could hardly wait to reach New York.

In New York loud noises on the streets frightened Fanny, but she walked bravely beside her mother.

Dr. Mott carefully checked Fanny's eyes. Then he slowly shook his head. "I'm afraid you will always be blind, Fanny," he said.

Sadly, Mrs. Crosby took Fanny home. Nothing else could be done.

Though she would never see, Fanny made up her mind to be happy. One day, after her eighth birthday, she made up a poem—

O what a happy soul am I,
   Although I cannot see,
I am resolved that in this world
   Contented I will be.

How many blessings I enjoy
   That other people don't
To weep and sigh because I'm blind,
   I cannot and I won't.

Fanny continued to make up poems. And day by day she began to wish that she could go to school. Fanny's grandmother kept on reading to her. Fanny carefully stored all she heard in her memory.

"Oh, I wish I could go to school and learn like other children do!" she said to herself.

One night after Grandmother had prayed with her, Fanny sat thinking about school and her blindness. She knew God answered prayer. She knelt and prayed, "Dear Lord, please show me how I can learn like other children." Then she went to bed.

A long time passed. One day Fanny opened the gate to the front yard. She heard a paper rustle.

"Mother?" Fanny asked.

"Yes, Fanny, it's Mother. The mailman was just here. He brought a letter for you from the New York Institute for the Blind. Would you like to go to school?"

"School!" Fanny cried. "Oh, Mother, I want to go to school more than anything in the world."

New Sight

At the New York Institute for the Blind, Fanny learned to read Braille. She studied English, arithmetic, and history. She made friends too.

More and more often she wrote poems. Since the class she liked best was music, she began singing some of her poems. Her new friends at the Institute joined her. Time seemed to pass quickly. Fanny enjoyed her life at the Institute.

When she grew up, she did not leave. Instead she took a job as a teacher at the Institute.

One Monday morning as she stood in front of the class, someone told her that one of the students was very ill. Fanny hurried to the student's room to visit her. The sick girl was too weak to sit up.

"Good-bye, Miss Crosby," she whispered.

The next morning the girl died.

The illness spread quickly. Fanny stopped teaching and became a nurse. Then she caught the illness herself. Fanny did not want anyone to worry, and so she said nothing about it. That night she went to bed early. By the next morning she was better.

But Fanny knew that if she had died from the illness, she would not have gone to heaven. She had never asked Christ to save her.

One night at church Fanny knew what she had to do.

Right then Fanny asked the Lord to forgive her sins and be her Saviour.

After that Fanny began writing more and more poems, only now they were all written for the Lord.

She remembered the Bible stories her grandmother had read to her. She wrote—

Tell me the story of Jesus,
  Write on my heart every word.
Tell me the story most precious
  Sweetest that ever was heard.

Christians everywhere enjoyed her poems.

A man named Al Van Alstyne heard Fanny's poems. Mr. Van Alstyne was blind too. He had been a student at the Institute years before. Now he had returned to teach music. While Fanny wrote poems, Mr. Van Alstyne wrote music for them. The two teachers became good friends. Then one day Mr. Van Alstyne asked Fanny to marry him. Soon Fanny left her teaching job to become a housewife.

Since she did not teach, Fanny had more time to write. Her poems soon became gospel songs when her husband wrote music for them. People in churches across America and in England sang them.

Fanny always thanked the Lord for helping her write. One of her songs says—

> This is my story,
> This is my song,
> Praising my Saviour
> All the day long.

Fanny certainly praised the Lord in song. By the end of her life she had written eight thousand gospel songs!

Though she lived in darkness because she was blind, she wanted to show others the light of God's Word. Once people were saved, they could sing with her—

Redeemed, how I love to proclaim it,
Redeemed by the blood of the Lamb.
Redeemed through his infinite mercy
His child and forever I am.

"Fanny," a preacher said to her, "it is too bad that God did not give you the gift of sight."

Fanny smiled. "Not so! Just think, the first face I will ever see will be the face of Christ my Saviour. I believe God intended that I should be blind so that I could praise Him better. If I had my sight, I might never have written my poems."

When Fanny was ninety-four years old, she went home to be with the Lord. She had written about heaven many years before—

And I shall see Him face to face,
And tell the story saved by grace.

The Musical Mulfingers

(a true story)

Chairs scraped as the eleven Mulfinger children sat down at the table.

"Mmmm," said Daniel above the clatter. "Soup! I like soup!"

Sara smiled at him across the table. "You like everything, Daniel."

"Well, almost everything," Daniel agreed.

The noise stopped as Mr. Mulfinger cleared his throat. "Let's pray," he said.

Thirteen heads bowed.

270

"Father," prayed Mr. Mulfinger, "we thank Thee for this food and for Thy blessings to us. Bless this food to our use, and bless our activities tonight, in Jesus' name. Amen."

For a few moments the normal chatter was hushed as thirteen spoons clanked in thirteen soup bowls. Then Martha looked up.

"Today I flew the kite higher than I ever have before," she said proudly.

"All by yourself?" asked Sara.

"Well," Martha admitted, "Mark helped a little."

"A little?" Mark grinned. "I helped a lot!"

"I'm glad you did, Mark," said his mother. "And, Daniel, thank you for the lovely flowers you picked for our table."

"It was thoughtful of you to bring flowers for your mother, Daniel," said Mr. Mulfinger. "I know she likes them a lot."

He looked across the table at Mrs. Mulfinger. "We need to practice if we are going to play at church next week," he added. "Tonight after devotions would be a good time to get started."

Mrs. Mulfinger nodded. "While Ruth and Sara help me wash the dishes, will you and the boys get the living room ready?" she said.

When everyone was finished eating, the girls cleared the table. Mark helped Mr. Mulfinger get the Bibles out of the cabinet.

Soon the room was quiet. From biggest to littlest everyone read from Psalms except Joanna, who could not read yet. Mr. Mulfinger stopped to explain some of the verses. Then he answered the children's

questions. They shared blessings from their day, and Mr. Mulfinger asked for prayer requests.

"Let's pray for our aunts and uncles who aren't saved," said Mary.

"Please pray for my children's chorus at church," said Mrs. Mulfinger.

"And for my teacher," added Daniel. "She's not feeling well."

More and more requests were added to those already given. Then Sharon and Ruth prayed, and Mr. Mulfinger closed the prayer.

"Come on, Mark and Daniel," Mr. Mulfinger said. "We will move the stuffed chairs out of the way and bring in the straight chairs while the girls wash and dry the dishes."

At last the dishes were done and the living room had become the Mulfinger rehearsal room. The children began to tune violins and cellos and flutes.

"Mark, your trombone slide almost knocked over Rachel's music stand!" said Mr. Mulfinger.

The girls giggled.

"Now is everyone ready?" Mr. Mulfinger asked.

Everyone nodded.

"Let's play 'Come, Thou Fount' first. Listen to your mother. She has the melody in her part."

Everyone tried to fit his part to the melody.

"Wait!" Mrs. Mulfinger stopped playing. "Someone made a mistake on that last part. Let's try it again from the beginning."

And so it went.

Each night the Mulfingers practiced after their devotions. Each night the music was played a little better. Then at last came the big night!

The Mulfingers took their instruments and music stands out to the car. The car soon filled up with big Mulfingers and little Mulfingers, big instruments and little instruments.

"Is everyone here?" called Mr. Mulfinger.

From oldest to youngest the children called out their names.

276

"That's everyone," said Mr. Mulfinger. "Let's pray before we leave."

After praying for a safe trip, Mr. Mulfinger drove out of the driveway. They were several blocks away when Mark called suddenly, "Stop, Dad! I forgot my trombone!'

"Mark," cried Mrs. Mulfinger. "How could you forget your trombone?"

"If we go back we will be late for church," Sara said.

"We can't set up our music stands after church begins!" said Martha.

"Wait, children. Don't you remember the verses we read last week? God will help us get there in time if we trust Him."

Mr. Mulfinger turned the car around. They went back and got Mark's trombone. Again they left the house.

It seemed as if every traffic light was green. It took less time to get to church than it usually did. When the Mulfingers arrived, they still had enough time to set up their music stands and tune their instruments.

"See what God can do when you turn your time over to Him, children?" whispered Mrs. Mulfinger.

The children smiled back at her. Then as Mrs. Mulfinger started to play "Come, Thou Fount," the children joined in. The notes from Mark's trombone blended with the music of the violins, cellos, and flutes as the hymn drifted through the quiet building.

And Mark didn't once knock over a music stand.

The Song of Happy People

Clinkety-clank, clinkety-clank. The baker's new pans went clinkety-clank.

Tippety-tap, tippety-tap. The shoemaker's hammer went tippety-tap.

Swishety-swoosh, swishety-swoosh. The weaver's long reeds went swishety-swoosh.

All the people in town were busy making music as they worked—everyone except Mr. McDoogle. He was much too old to work. Every day he sat on his porch and patted his bony knee in time to the clank of the baker's new pans, the tap of the shoemaker's hammer, and the swoosh of the weaver's long reeds. He never missed a beat.

"Ah," he would say, leaning back in his old chair. "The song of happy people at work is a good sound."

Then one day a stranger crept into town. His dark suit blended in well with the shadows. Only Mr. McDoogle saw him creeping down Main Street, glancing this way and that.

"That man is up to no good," Mr. McDoogle said to himself. "He need not think that he will get into my house."

The stranger pushed open the door to the baker's shop, letting the clinkety-clank of the baker's pans float down the street.

"Good morning, stranger," said the baker, clapping his hands together till a cloud of flour choked him.

"What's good about it?" the stranger grumbled. "It's too chilly outside. Your rolls might not rise on a day like this."

The baker scratched his nose. Then he sat down on a stool. "What will I do if my rolls won't rise?" he wailed.

"Close up shop till the air is just right," said the stranger. Then he slipped out the door. The baker followed him, locking the door as he went.

The stranger hurried quickly down the street. Into the shoemaker's shop he went, letting the tippety-tap of the shoemaker's hammer float down the street.

"Good morning, stranger," said the shoe-maker, jumping up and scattering tacks into the cracks of the floor.

"What's good about it?" the stranger muttered. He shook his head. "Times are bad, bad, bad. Everything costs too much. And now you might not have the tacks you need to finish the job."

The shoemaker looked into the almost empty pockets of his apron and sighed. "What will I do if I don't have the tacks I need?"

"Close up shop till prices come down," said the stranger. Then he vanished out the door. The shoemaker followed him, locking the door as he went.

The stranger lost no time in making his way to the weaver's shop. The bell tinkled as he pushed open the door. The swishety-swoosh of the weaver's long reeds floated into the air.

"Good morning, stranger," said the weaver, stepping on a reed and snapping it in two.

"What's good about it?" the stranger growled. "You just broke a reed. All of your reeds might be too brittle to make baskets."

The weaver's brown eyes opened wide. "What should I do if my reeds are too brittle?" he cried.

The stranger shrugged. "Better close up shop. You might never have soft reeds." He scuttled out the door. The weaver followed him, locking the door as he went.

The stranger started back up Main Street. Behind him came the baker, wringing his hands. Behind the baker came the shoemaker, twisting his apron. Behind the shoemaker came the weaver, biting his fingernails. No one was making any music because no one was working. No one was working because everyone was thinking, "What if . . . ."

Right up to Mr. McDoogle's house they went. Mr. McDoogle was sitting on his porch, but his hand was not patting his bony knee. "Something is not right," he called out. "I do not hear the song of happy people any more. I do not hear the clinkety-clank of the baker's new pans or the tippety-tap of the shoemaker's hammer or the swishety-swoosh of the weaver's long reeds."

"But what if my rolls won't rise . . ."

"Or I do not have the tacks I need . . ."

"Or my reeds are too brittle?"

"Plan your work and work your plan," said old Mr. McDoogle. "Do what you have to do to get the job finished. And remember," he said, pointing to the stranger slinking out of sight, "fear is never a good friend."

The baker clapped his hands. "I can let my rolls rise in a warm oven."

The shoemaker snapped his fingers. "I can pick up the tacks I spilled."

The weaver put his hands on his hips. "I can soak my brittle reeds in water till they are soft."

The three friends set off down Main Street, singing happily. And old Mr. McDoogle leaned back in his chair, patting his bony knee in time to the song of happy people.

GLOSSARY

This glossary has information about selected words found in this reader. You can find meanings of words as they are used in the stories. Certain unusual words such as foreign names are included so you can pronounce them correctly when you read.

The pronunciation symbols below show how to pronounce each vowel and several of the less familiar consonants.

ă	pat	ĕ	pet	î	fierce
ā	pay	ē	be	ŏ	pot
â	care	ĭ	pit	ō	go
ä	father	ī	pie	ô	paw, for

oi	oil	ŭ	cut	zh	vision
o͝o	book	û	fur	ə	ago, item,
o͞o	boot	*th*	the		pencil, atom,
yo͞o	abuse	th	thin		circus
ou	out	hw	which	ər	butter

a·board | ə **bôrd'** | or | ə **bōrd'** | On, onto, or inside a ship.

ad·mi·ral | **ăd'** mər əl | The commander-in-chief of a fleet.

a·dopt | ə **dŏpt'** | To take a person or animal into one's family.

an·nounc·er | ə **noun'** sər | A person whose job is to speak to the public on radio or television.

ar·mor | **är'** mər | A covering for the body, usually made of metal.

at·ten·dant | ə **tĕn'** dənt | A person who waits on another.

announcer

bal·ance | **băl'** əns | 1. A steady or stable position: *I almost lost my balance.* 2. To hold in a steady or stable position.

ban·ish | **băn'** ish | To force a person or thing to leave a place; to drive away.

bat·tle·field | **băt'** l fēld' | An area where a battle is fought.

bat·tle·ship | **băt'** l shĭp' | A large warship having very heavy guns and armor.

beam | bēm | To smile widely.

black·smith | **blăk'** smĭth' | A person who makes things out of iron.

blade | blād | The thin, flat part of something.

blacksmith

287

bolt | bōlt | To fasten or lock with a bolt or bolts.

Braille | brāl | A system of writing and printing for blind people.

brass | brăs | A yellowish metal that contains copper and zinc.

bray | brā | To utter a loud, harsh cry, as a donkey.

Brit·ish | **brĭt′** ish | Of Great Britain and its people.

brit·tle | **brĭt′** l | Hard and easy to break; not flexible.

can·teen | kăn tēn′ | A container for carrying drinking water or other liquids.

can·vas | **kăn′** vəs | A heavy, coarse cloth used for making tents, sails, etc.

cap·tain | **kăp′** tən | The leader of a group.

car·a·mel | **kăr′** ə məl | A brown syrup made by cooking sugar; used to color and flavor foods.

cast | kăst | or | käst | 1. A stiff bandage, usually made of gauze coated with plaster. 2. The actors in a play.

cel·lar | **sĕl′** ər | A room under a building where things are stored.

cel·lo | **chĕl′** ō | A musical instrument of the violin family.

char·i·ot | **chăr′** ē ət | A two-wheeled vehicle pulled by horses.

chime | chīm | A musical sound made by bells.

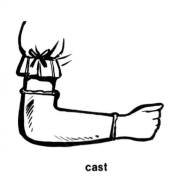

cast

ă	pat	ĕ	pet
ā	pay	ē	be
â	care	ĭ	pit
ä	father	ī	pie
î	fierce	oi	oil
ŏ	pot	о͝о	book
ō	go	о͞о	boot
ô	paw,	yо͞о	abuse
	for	ou	out
ŭ	cut	zh	vision
û	fur	ə	ago, item,
th	the		pencil, atom,
th	thin		circus
hw	which	ər	butter

clin·ic | klĭn′ ĭk | A place that gives medical help to patients not staying in the hospital.

clump | klŭmp | To walk with a heavy, dull sound.

cob·ble·stone | kŏb′ əl stōn | A round stone once used to cover streets.

co·lo·nel | kûr′ nəl | An officer in the Army, Air Force, or Marine Corps. A colonel ranks above a major and below a general.

Co·los·sians | kə lŏsh′ ənz | The twelfth book of the New Testament.

com·mend | kə mĕnd′ | To show to be desirable.

crow's nest

com·pe·ti·tion | kŏm′ pĭ tĭsh′ ən | A contest of skill and ability.

con·cern | kən sûrn′ | Serious care or interest.

con·cert | kŏn′ sûrt′ | or | kŏn′ sərt | A performance of music given by a number of musicians.

con·cen·trate | kŏn′ sən trāt′ | To keep one's mind, attention, or efforts on something.

cour·age | kûr′ ĭj | A quality of character that makes a person able to face danger or hardship without fear or in spite of fear.

court | kôrt | or | kōrt | The attendants, advisors, and other people who work for a king.

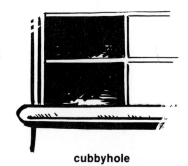

cubbyhole

crow's-nest | krōz′ nĕst′ | A small platform near the top of a ship's mast, used by sailors for seeing long distances.

cub·by·hole | kŭb′ ē hōl | A small nook in a desk or other piece of furniture.

deck

dike

dawn | dôn | 1. The first light that shows in the morning; daybreak. 2. To begin to grow light in the morning.

de·clare | dĭ **klâr** | To state strongly; stress; affirm.

deck | dĕk | The floor of a ship.

de·light | dĭ **līt'** | Great pleasure; joy.

de·vo·tions | dĭ vō' shənz | A time of Bible reading and prayer.

dis·ci·ple | dĭ **sī'** pəl | One of the twelve chosen *disciples* of Jesus Christ. The disciples helped to spread the teachings of Jesus.

driz·zle | **drĭz'** əl | A gentle rain-like mist.

dike | dīk | A wall, dam, or embankment built to hold back water and prevent flooding.

em·per·or | **ĕm'** pər ər | A man who rules an empire.

em·pire | **ĕm'** pīr | A group of countries under one ruler or government.

e·nor·mous | ĭ **nor'** məs | Huge.

e·ter·nal | ĭ **tûr'** nəl | Without beginning or end.

ă	pat	ĕ	pet
ā	pay	ē	be
â	care	ĭ	pit
ä	father	ī	pie
î	fierce	oi	oil
ŏ	pot	o͝o	book
ō	go	o͞o	boot
ô	paw,	yo͞o	abuse
	for	ou	out
ŭ	cut	zh	vision
û	fur	ə	ago, item,
th	the		pencil,atom,
th	thin		circus
hw	which	ər	butter

fa·ble | **fā'** bəl | A legendary story that teaches a lesson. Often the characters in fables are animals that talk and act like people.

faint | fānt | 1. Dizzy and weak. 2. To become dizzy and weak; to seem to fall asleep suddenly for a short while.

flag·ship | flăg′ shĭp′ | A ship in a fleet that bears the flag or standard of the fleet.

flan | flăn | or | flän | A Spanish dessert made with caramel.

flap·jack | flăp′ jăk | A pancake.

fleet | flēt | A group of ships.

flick·er | flĭk′ ər | To give a weak, unsteady light.

flood | flŭd | 1. A great overflow of water onto a place that is usually dry. 2. To cover or fill with water.

fort | fôrt | or | fōrt | An area or building that has been made strong against possible attacks by enemies.

flapjacks

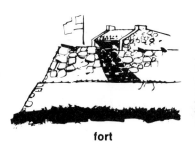

fort

G

gal·lant | găl′ ənt | Brave and good; courageous.

gen·er·al | jĕn′ ər əl | A high-ranking army officer.

glow | glō | 1. To give off a steady light; shine. 2. A rosy, healthy color.

grace | grās | In the Bible, the undeserved kindness given to repentant sinners because of the death of Jesus Christ on the cross.

grid·dle | grĭd′ l | A flat metal surface or pan for cooking bacon.

gush | gŭsh | To flow or pour out all of a sudden and in great quantity.

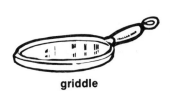

griddle

hail¹ | hāl | Small rounded pieces of ice that fall to earth, usually during thunderstorms.

hail² | hāl | To call to in greeting or welcome.

har·bor | här′ bər | A sheltered place along a coast serving as a port for ships.

har·ness | här′ nĭs | A set of leather straps and metal pieces by which an ox is attached to a plow.

hitch | hĭch | To tie or fasten with a rope or strap.

hold | hōld | A space inside a ship or airplane where cargo is carried.

hol·low | hŏl′ ō | Having an empty space inside.

hur·ri·cane | hûr′ ĭ kān′ | A powerful storm with very strong winds and heavy rains.

harness

ă	pat	ĕ	pet	
ā	pay	ē	be	
â	care	ĭ	pit	
ä	father	ī	pie	
î	fierce	oi	oil	
ŏ	pot	o͝o	book	
ō	go	o͞o	boot	
ô	paw,	yo͞o	abuse	
	for	ou	out	
ŭ	cut	zh	vision	
û	fur	ə	ago, item,	
th	the		pencil,atom,	
th	thin		circus	
hw	which	ər	butter	

in·fi·nite | ĭn′ fə nĭt | Having no limit or end.

in·spect | ĭn spekt′ | To look at or examine carefully.

in·sti·tute | ĭn′ stĭ to͞ot′ | or | ĭn′ stĭ tyo͞ot′ | An organization set up for some special purpose.

in·ter·rupt | ĭn tə rŭpt′ | To break in on.

in·vade | ĭn vād′ | To enter with force; attack.

Juan·i·ta | hwä **nē′** tə | A Spanish name for a girl.

knap·sack | **năp′** săk′ | A leather bag made to be worn on the back. A knapsack is used to carry supplies.

knapsack

laun·dry | **lôn′** drē | or | **län′** drē | Clothes and linens that need to be washed or have been washed.

lav·en·der | **lăv′** ən dər | A plant with small, fragrant purplish flowers. Oil from these flowers is used to make perfume. The dried flowers are sometimes used to give clothing and linens a pleasant smell.

lep·er | **lĕp′** ər | One who has the disease of leprosy.

lep·ro·sy | **lĕp′** rə sē | An incurable disease that spreads over the skin.

lieu·ten·ant | lo͞o **ten′** ənt | An officer in the Army, Air Force, or Marine Corps ranking below a captain.

lieutenant

long·ing | **lông′** ĭng | A deep wish; a strong desire.

lum·ber | **lŭm′** bər | To move or walk in a clumsy and often noisy manner.

293

lumberjack

lum·ber·jack | lŭm′ bər jăk′ | A person whose work is to chop down trees and get the logs to a sawmill.

lum·ber·yard | lŭm′ bər yärd′ | A place where lumber is kept and sold.

mast | măst | or | mäst | A tall pole for the sails and rigging of a sailing ship.

mead·ow·lark | měd′ ō lärk′ | A North American songbird. It has a brownish back and a yellow breast with a black marking shaped like a *v*.

med·i·cine | měd′ ĭ sĭn | Any substance used to treat or prevent disease and relieve pain.

mel·o·dy | měl′ ə dē | A group of musical tones in a pleasing order; a tune.

mer·cy | mûr′ sē | Kind treatment when it is not deserved.

mir·a·cle | mĭr′ ə kəl | A supernatural event beyond or outside God's ordinary method of working in the natural world.

mis·tress | mĭs′ trĭs | A woman who is the head of a household.

muf·fled | mŭf′ ld | Softened: *the muffled bark of a dog.*

mu·si·cian | myoō zĭsh′ ən | One who is skilled in playing or composing music.

mus·sel | mŭs′ əl | A water animal with a soft body and a pair of narrow, dark blue shells. Some mussels are used as food.

mussel

ă	pat	ĕ	pet
ā	pay	ē	be
â	care	ĭ	pit
ä	father	ī	pie
î	fierce	oi	oil
ŏ	pot	oō	book
ō	go	ōō	boot
ô	paw, for	yōō	abuse
		ou	out
ŭ	cut	zh	vision
û	fur	ə	ago, item, pencil, atom, circus
th	the		
th	thin		
hw	which	ər	butter

294

mut·ter | mŭt′ ər | To speak or say in a low voice that is not clear; mumble.

mys·te·ry | mĭs′ tə rē | Anything that is not known or understood; a secret.

nar·ra·tor | năr′ ā ter | or | nă rā′ tər | or | năr′ ə ter | One who gives an oral or written account; one who tells a story.

night·in·gale | nīt′ n gāl′ | or | nī′ tǐng gāl′ | A brownish bird of Europe and Asia. The nightingale has a sweet song and often sings at night.

nightingale

nudge | nŭj | To poke or push in a gentle way.

oar | ôr | or | ōr | A long, thin pole with a flat blade at one end. Oars are used to row and steer boats.

o·cean | ō′ shən | The great mass of salt water that covers almost three quarters of the earth's surface.

op·er·a·tion | ŏp′ ə rā′ shən | A process of treatment for diseases and disorders of the living body by using surgery.

oar

pace | pās | To walk back and forth.

peer | pîr | To look closely in order to see something clearly.

per·il·ous | pěr′ ə ləs | Dangerous.

295

pin·cush·ion | pĭn′ kŏosh′ ən | A small, firm cushion or ball in which pins and needles are stuck when they are not being used.

pipe | pīp | To carry or send by means of a pipe.

pledge | plĕj | A formal promise; a vow.

proph·et | prŏf′ it | In the Bible, one who spoke a message given to him by God.

pry | prī | To raise or move by force.

psalm | säm | A song or poem that gives praise to God.

psal·ter·y | sôl′ tə rē | A stringed instrument used in Bible times, played by plucking the strings.

puz·zled | pŭz′ əld | Confused.

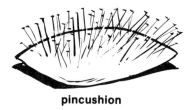

pincushion

quill | kwĭl | A long, stiff feather usually from the tail or wing of a bird.

ram·part | răm′ pärt | A wall of protection.

ra·tion | răsh′ ən | or | rā′ shən | A fixed amount or portion of food for a person or animal.

re·deem | rĭ dēm′ | To buy back or rescue something that was lost.

reed | rēd | Any of several tall grasses or similar plants that have hollow stems.

re·hearse | rĭ hûrs′ | To practice all or part of a program in order to prepare for a performance.

ă	pat	ĕ	pet
ā	pay	ē	be
â	care	ĭ	pit
ä	father	ī	pie
î	fierce	oi	oil
ŏ	pot	ŏŏ	book
ō	go	ōō	boot
ô	paw,	yōō	abuse
	for	ou	out
ŭ	cut	zh	vision
û	fur	ə	ago, item,
th	the		pencil,atom,
th	thin		circus
hw	which	ər	butter

296

re·joice | rĭ **jois′** | To feel or show joy.

re·lease | rĭ **lēs′** | To set free.

rick·e·ty | **rĭk′** ĭt ē | Unstable; shaky; about to fall apart.

right·eous | **rī′** chəs | Doing that which is right in the sight of God; hating sin and loving good.

rus·tle | **rŭs′** əl | To make or cause to make a soft, fluttering or crackling sound.

S

Sab·bath | **săb′** əth | The seventh day of the week, which God commanded the Jews in the Old Testament to observe as a day of rest. Christians worship on Sunday in observance of Christ's resurrection from the dead on the first day of the week.

sea anemone

scale | skāl | One of the small, thin parts that form the skin of fish and some reptiles.

scam·per | **skăm′** pər | To run quickly.

scent | sĕnt | A particular smell.

scram·ble | **skrăm′** bəl | To move quickly, especially by climbing or crawling.

scur·ry | **skûr′** ē | To run or move about quickly.

sea a·nem·o·ne | sē ə **nĕm′** ə nē | A sea animal with a flexible body shaped like a tube.

sea ur·chin | sē **ûr′** chĭn | A round, soft-bodied sea animal covered with quill-like spikes.

sea urchin

seep | sēp | To spread or pass through slowly; ooze.

shed

ses·sion | sĕsh′ ən | A meeting or series of meetings.

shed | shĕd | A small, simple building for storage or shelter.

shield | shēld | A piece of armor carried in olden times by a warrior to protect against an enemy's blows.

shiv·er | shĭv′ ər | To shake or tremble from cold or fear, in a way one cannot control.

shuf·fle | shŭf′ əl | To walk by dragging the feet along the ground.

sí | sē | The Spanish word for *yes*.

skip | skĭp | To pass quickly over or leave out.

sling | slĭng | To put, carry, or hang in a sling.

sol·dier | sōl′ jər | A person who serves in the army.

spike | spīk | A long, thick, sharp-pointed object.

stale | stāl | Not fresh; having lost flavor.

Star-Span·gled Ban·ner | stär spăng′gəld băn′ər | The flag of the United States.

sub·ject | sŭb′ jĭkt | A person under the rule of another.

swoop | swo͞op | To fly or move with a quick, sudden, sweeping motion.

ta·co | tä′ kō | A round, flat Mexican bread that is folded in half and stuffed with a filling such as meat or cheese.

ă	pat	ĕ	pet
ā	pay	ē	be
â	care	ĭ	pit
ä	father	ī	pie
î	fierce	oi	oil
ŏ	pot	o͝o	book
ō	go	o͞o	boot
ô	paw, for	yo͞o	abuse
		ou	out
ŭ	cut	zh	vision
û	fur	ə	ago, item, pencil, atom, circus
th	the		
th	thin		
hw	which	ər	butter

tai·lor | tā′ lər | A person who makes, repairs, or alters clothes.

tem·per | tĕm′ pər | The condition of being calm in the mind or emotions.

ten·ta·cle | tĕn′ tə kəl | One of the thin flexible parts that extend from the body of an octopus, jellyfish, or other animal. Tentacles are used for grasping and moving.

tes·ti·mo·ny | tĕs′ tə mō nē | A public statement by a person about how God has blessed him.

trail | trāl | To follow.

trom·bone | trŏm **bōn′** | or | **trŏm′** bōn | A brass wind musical instrument, like the trumpet but with two long tubes shaped like *U*s and having a lower pitch.

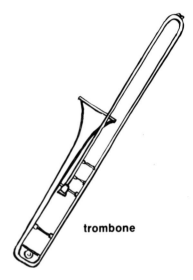

trombone

truce flag | trōōs′ flăg | A flag signifying a temporary stop in fighting.

trudge | trŭj | To walk slowly with effort.

trum·pet | trŭm′ pĭt | 1. A brass wind instrument that has a strong tone with a high pitch. 2. To make a loud, high sound like a trumpet.

twi·light | twī′ līt | The period of time when the sun is below the horizon but there is a little light in the sky.

un·grate·ful | ŭn **grāt′** fəl | Not grateful; without thanks.

up·right | ŭp′ rīt′ | Good and honest.

va·cant | vā′ kənt | Empty.

va·cuum | văk′ yo͞om | To clean with a machine that sucks up dirt into a bag.

van·ish | văn′ ĭsh | To disappear; become invisible.

vil·lage | vĭl′ ĭj | A group of houses that make up a community smaller than a town.

weaver

wa·ter pump | wô′ tər pŭmp | A metal device with a handle, used to pump water out from an underground well.

wea·ry | wîr′ ē | Needing rest; tired.

weav·er | wē′ vər | One who makes cloth or other items by passing strands under and over other strands.

whim·per | hwĭm′ pər | or | wĭm′ pər | To cry with weak, broken, whining sounds.

whip | hwĭp | or | wĭp | To move suddenly and quickly.

wil·der·ness | wĭl′ dər nĭs | A wild place or region that is not lived in by people.

wisp | wĭsp | A faint streak of smoke.

wound | wo͞ond | An injury, especially when the skin is broken.

wor·ship | wûr′ shĭp | To love and obey God from the heart.

wretch | rĕch | A hopeless, miserable person.

wring | rĭng | To twist and squeeze.

ă	pat	ĕ	pet
ā	pay	ē	be
â	care	ĭ	pit
ä	father	ī	pie
î	fierce	oi	oil
ŏ	pot	o͞o	book
ō	go	o͞o	boot
ô	paw,	yo͞o	abuse
	for	ou	out
ŭ	cut	zh	vision
û	fur	ə	ago, item,
th	the		pencil, atom,
th	thin		circus
hw	which	ər	butter

300